A Radically Modern Approach to Introductory Physics
Second Edition

Volume 1: Fundamental Principles

David J. Raymond

The New Mexico Tech Press

Socorro, New Mexico, USA

A Radically Modern Approach to Introductory Physics
Second Edition
Volume 1: Fundamental Principles

David J. Raymond

Second Edition
Original state, 17 May 2016

Publisher's Cataloguing-in-Publication Data

```
Raymond, David J.
   A radically modern approach to introductory physics, second edition:
   Volume 1: Fundamental principles / David J. Raymond.
   xii, 227 p.: ill. ; 28 cm
   Preface -- Waves in one dimension -- Waves in two and three
   dimensions -- Geometrical optics -- Special relativity -- Applications
   of special relativity -- Acceleration and general relativity --
   Matter waves -- Geometrical optics and Newton's Laws -- Symmetry
   and bound states -- Dynamics of multiple particles -- Rotational
   dynamics -- Harmonic oscillator -- Constants, units and conversions
   ISBN 978-1-938159-06-0 (print) -- 978-1-938159-07-7 (ebook)
   1. Physics.  2. Waves.  3. Wave mechanics.  4. Mathematical
   physics.  5. Relativity (Physics).  I. Title.
QC23.R268 2016 v.1 (print) -- QC23.R268 2016eb v.1 (ebook)
```

OCLC Number: 952471268 (print) – 952469817 (ebook)

Published by The New Mexico Tech Press, a New Mexico nonprofit corporation
This copy printed by CreateSpace, Charleston, SC

The New Mexico Tech Press
Socorro, New Mexico, USA
http://press.nmt.edu

To my wife Georgia and my daughters Maria and Elizabeth.

Contents

Preface

The idea for a "radically modern" introductory physics course arose out of frustration in the physics department at New Mexico Tech with the standard two-semester treatment of the subject. It is basically impossible to incorporate a significant amount of "modern physics" (meaning post-19th century!) in that format. It seemed to us that largely skipping the "interesting stuff" that has transpired since the days of Einstein and Bohr was like teaching biology without any reference to DNA. We felt at the time (and still feel) that an introductory physics course for non-majors should make an attempt to cover the great accomplishments of physics in the 20th century, since they form such an important part of our scientific culture.

It would, of course, be easy to pander to students – teach them superficially about the things they find interesting, while skipping the "hard stuff". However, I am convinced that they would ultimately find such an approach as unsatisfying as would the educated physicist. What was needed was a unifying vision which allowed the presentation of all of physics from a modern point of view.

The idea for this course came from reading Louis de Broglie's Nobel Prize address.[1] De Broglie's work is a masterpiece based on the principles of optics and special relativity, which qualitatively foresees the path taken by Schrödinger and others in the development of quantum mechanics. It thus dawned on me that perhaps optics and waves together with relativity could form a better foundation for all of physics, providing a more interesting way into the subject than classical mechanics.

Whether this is so or not is still a matter of debate, but it is indisputable that such a path is much more fascinating to most college students interested in pursuing studies in physics — especially those who have been through the

---

[1]Reprinted in: Boorse, H. A., and L. Motz, 1966: *The world of the atom*. Basic Books, New York, 1873 pp. Also, search for "Louis de Broglie Nobel Prize Address" on the web.

usual high school treatment of classical mechanics. I am also convinced that the development of physics in these terms, though not historical, is at least as rigorous and coherent as the classical approach.

After 15 years of gradual development, it is clear that the course failed in its original purpose, as a replacement for the standard, one-year introductory physics course with calculus. The material is way too challenging, given the level of interest of the typical non-physics student. However, the course has found a niche at the sophomore level for physics majors (and occasional non-majors with a special interest in physics) to explore some of the ideas that drew them to physics in the first place. It was placed at the sophomore level because we found that having some background in both calculus and introductory college-level physics is advantageous for most students. However, we allow incoming freshmen into the course if they have an appropriate high school background in physics and math.

The course is tightly structured, and it contains little or nothing that can be omitted. However, it is designed to fit into two semesters or three quarters. In broad outline form, the structure is as follows:

- Optics and waves occur first on the menu. The idea of group velocity is central to the entire course, and is introduced in the first chapter. This is a difficult topic, but repeated reviews through the year cause it eventually to sink in. Interference and diffraction are done in a reasonably conventional manner. Geometrical optics is introduced, not only for its practical importance, but also because classical mechanics is later introduced as the geometrical optics limit of quantum mechanics.

- Relativity is treated totally in terms of space-time diagrams – the Lorentz transformations seem to me to be quite confusing to students at this level ("Does gamma go upstairs or downstairs?"), and all desired results can be obtained by using the "space-time Pythagorean theorem" instead, with much better effect.

- Relativity plus waves leads to a dispersion relation for free matter waves. Optics in a region of variable refractive index provides a powerful analogy for the quantum mechanics of a particle subject to potential energy. The group velocity of waves is equated to the particle velocity, leading to the classical limit and Newton's equations. The basic topics of classical mechanics are then done in a more or less conventional, though abbreviated fashion.

- Gravity is treated conventionally, except that Gauss's law is introduced for the gravitational field. This is useful in and of itself, but also provides a preview of its deployment in electromagnetism. The repetition is useful pedagogically.

- Electromagnetism is treated in a highly unconventional way, though the endpoint is Maxwell's equations in their usual integral form. The connection to relativity is exploited rather than buried. In particular, the seemingly simple question of how potential energy can be extended to the relativistic context gives rise to the idea of potential momentum. The potential energy and potential momentum together form a four-vector which is closely related to the scalar and vector potential of electromagnetism. The Aharonov-Bohm effect is easily explained using the idea of potential momentum in one dimension, while extension to three dimensions results in a version of Snell's law valid for matter waves, from which the Lorentz force law is derived.

- The generation of electromagnetic fields comes from Coulomb's law plus relativity (I borrowed from my graduate advisor Mel Schwartz's text on electromagnetism here), with the scalar and vector potential being used to produce a much more straightforward treatment than is possible with electric and magnetic fields. Electromagnetic radiation is a lot simpler in terms of the potential fields as well.

- Resistors, capacitors, and inductors are treated for their practical value, but also because their consideration leads to an understanding of energy in electromagnetic fields.

- At this point the book shifts to a more qualitative (but non-trivial) treatment of atoms, atomic nuclei, the standard model of elementary particles, and techniques for observing the very small. Ideas from optics, waves, and relativity reappear here. The Bohr model of the hydrogen atom is *not* presented for the simple reason that it gets the angular momentum of the electron wrong!

- The final section of the course deals with heat and statistical mechanics. Only at this point do non-conservative forces appear in the context of classical mechanics. Counting as a way to compute the entropy is introduced, and is applied to the Einstein model of a collection of harmonic oscillators (conceptualized as a "brick"), and in a limited way to an ideal gas. The second law of thermodynamics follows. The book ends with a fairly conventional treatment of heat engines.

A few words about how I have taught the course at New Mexico Tech are in order. As with our standard course, each week contains three lecture hours and a two-hour recitation. The recitation is the key to making the course accessible to the students. I generally have small groups of students working on assigned homework problems during recitation while I wander around giving hints. After all groups have completed their work, a representative from each group explains their problem to the class. The students are then required to write up the problems on their own and hand them in at a later date. The problems are the key to student learning, and associating course credit with the successful solution of these problems insures virtually 100% attendance in recitation.

In addition, chapter reading summaries are required, with the students urged to ask questions about material in the text that gave them difficulties. Significant lecture time is taken up answering these questions. Students tend to do the summaries, as they also count for their grade. The summaries and the questions posed by the students have been quite helpful to me in indicating parts of the text which need clarification.

The writing style of the text is quite terse. This partially reflects its origin in a set of lecture notes, but it also focuses the students' attention on what is really important. Given this structure, a knowledgeable instructor able to offer one-on-one time with students (as in our recitation sections) is essential for student success. The text is most likely to be useful in a sophomore-level course introducing physics majors to the broad world of physics viewed from a modern perspective.

I freely acknowledge stealing ideas from Edwin Taylor, John Archibald Wheeler, Thomas Moore, Robert Mills, Bruce Sherwood, and many other creative physicists, and I owe a great debt to them. The physics department at New Mexico Tech has been quite supportive of my efforts over the years relative to this course, for which I am exceedingly grateful. Finally, my humble thanks go out to the students who have enthusiastically (or on occasion unenthusiastically) responded to this course. It is much, much better as a result of their input.

My colleagues Alan Blyth, David Westpfahl, Ken Eack, and Sharon Sessions were brave enough to teach this course at various stages of its development, and I welcome the feedback I have received from them. Their experience shows that even seasoned physics teachers require time and effort to come to grips with the content of this textbook!

The reviews of Allan Stavely and Paul Arendt in conjunction with the publication of this book by the New Mexico Tech Press have been enormously helpful, and I am very thankful for their support and enthusiasm. Penny Bencomo and Keegan Livoti taught me a lot about written English with their copy editing.

David J. Raymond

Preface to Second Edition

Aside from numerous corrections, clarifications, and minor enhancements, the main additions to this edition include the following:

- The treatment of the harmonic oscillator is expanded, with complex exponential solutions, damped and forced oscillators, and several new problems.

- The discussion of Faraday's law is enhanced, with a distinction being made between EMFs generated by changing magnetic fluxes through fixed loops and those generated by magnetic forces on charge moving through translating or deforming loops.

- A section on angular momentum and magnetic moments is added to the chapter on atoms. The Stern-Gerlach experiment is treated in a problem.

As in the first edition, I am greatful for the reviews of Paul Arendt and Allan Stavely, who always manage to catch things that I have overlooked.

David J. Raymond
Physics Department
New Mexico Tech
Socorro, NM, USA
djraymondnm@gmail.com

Chapter 1

Waves in One Dimension

The wave is a universal phenomenon which occurs in a multitude of physical contexts. The purpose of this section is to describe the *kinematics* of waves, i. e., to provide tools for describing the form and motion of all waves irrespective of their underlying physical mechanisms.

Many examples of waves are well known to you. You undoubtedly know about ocean waves and have probably played with a stretched slinky toy, producing undulations which move rapidly along the slinky. Other examples of waves are sound, vibrations in solids, and light.

In this chapter we learn first about the basic properties of waves and introduce a special type of wave called the sine wave. Examples of waves seen in the real world are presented. We then learn about the superposition principle, which allows us to construct complex wave patterns by superimposing sine waves. Using these ideas, we discuss the related ideas of beats and interferometry. Finally, the ideas of wave packets and group velocity are introduced.

1.1 Transverse and Longitudinal Waves

With the exception of light, waves are undulations in a material medium. For instance, ocean waves are (nearly) vertical undulations in the position of water parcels. The oscillations in neighboring parcels are phased such that a *pattern* moves across the ocean surface. Waves on a slinky are either *transverse*, in that the motion of the material of the slinky is perpendicular to the orientation of the slinky, or they are *longitudinal*, with material motion in the

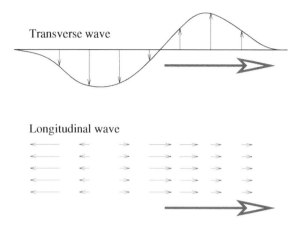

Figure 1.1: Example of displacements in transverse and longitudinal waves. The wave motion is to the right as indicated by the large arrows. The small arrows indicate the displacements at a particular instant.

direction of the stretched slinky. (See figure 1.1.) Some media support only longitudinal waves, others support only transverse waves, while yet others support both types. Light waves are purely transverse, while sound waves are purely longitudinal. Ocean waves are a peculiar mixture of transverse and longitudinal, with parcels of water moving in elliptical trajectories as waves pass.

Light is a form of electromagnetic radiation. The undulations in an electromagnetic wave occur in the electric and magnetic fields. These oscillations are perpendicular to the direction of motion of the wave (in a vacuum), which is why we call light a transverse wave.

1.2 Sine Waves

A particularly simple kind of wave, the sine wave, is illustrated in figure 1.2. This has the mathematical form

$$h(x) = h_0 \sin(2\pi x/\lambda), \tag{1.1}$$

where h is the *displacement* (which can be either longitudinal or transverse), h_0 is the maximum displacement, also called the *amplitude* of the wave, and

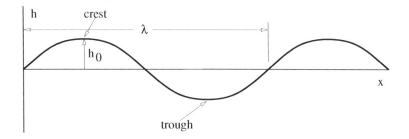

Figure 1.2: Definition sketch for a sine wave, showing the wavelength λ and the amplitude h_0 and the phase ϕ at various points.

λ is the *wavelength*. The oscillatory behavior of the wave is assumed to carry on to infinity in both positive and negative x directions. Notice that the wavelength is the distance through which the sine function completes one full cycle. The *crest* and the *trough* of a wave are the locations of the maximum and minimum displacements, as seen in figure 1.2.

So far we have only considered a sine wave as it appears at a particular time. All interesting waves move with time. The movement of a sine wave to the right a distance d may be accounted for by replacing x in the above formula by $x - d$. If this movement occurs in time t, then the wave moves at velocity $c = d/t$. Solving this for d and substituting yields a formula for the displacement of a sine wave as a function of both distance x and time t:

$$h(x, t) = h_0 \sin[2\pi(x - ct)/\lambda]. \tag{1.2}$$

The time for a wave to move one wavelength is called the *period* of the wave: $T = \lambda/c$. Thus, we can also write

$$h(x, t) = h_0 \sin[2\pi(x/\lambda - t/T)]. \tag{1.3}$$

Physicists actually like to write the equation for a sine wave in a slightly simpler form. Defining the *wavenumber* as $k = 2\pi/\lambda$ and the *angular frequency* as $\omega = 2\pi/T$, we write

$$h(x, t) = h_0 \sin(kx - \omega t). \tag{1.4}$$

We normally think of the frequency of oscillatory motion as the number of cycles completed per second. This is called the *rotational frequency*, and is given by $f = 1/T$. It is related to the angular frequency by $\omega = 2\pi f$. The rotational frequency is usually easier to measure than the angular frequency, but the angular frequency tends to be used more often in theoretical discussions. As shown above, converting between the two is not difficult. Rotational frequency is measured in units of hertz, abbreviated Hz; 1 Hz = 1 cycle s^{-1}. Angular frequency also has the dimensions of inverse time, e. g., radian s^{-1}, but the term "hertz" is generally reserved only for rotational frequency.

The argument of the sine function is by definition an angle. We refer to this angle as the *phase* of the wave, $\phi = kx - \omega t$. The difference in the phase of a wave at fixed time over a distance of one wavelength is 2π, as is the difference in phase at fixed position over a time interval of one wave period.

Since angles are dimensionless, we normally don't include this in the units for frequency. However, it sometimes clarifies things to refer to the dimensions of rotational frequency as "rotations per second" or angular frequency as "radians per second".

As previously noted, we call h_0, the maximum displacement of the wave, the amplitude. Often we are interested in the *intensity* of a wave, which is proportional to the square of the amplitude. The intensity is often related to the amount of energy being carried by a wave.

The wave speed we have defined above, $c = \lambda/T$, is actually called the *phase speed*. Since $\lambda = 2\pi/k$ and $T = 2\pi/\omega$, we can write the phase speed in terms of the angular frequency and the wavenumber:

$$c = \frac{\omega}{k} \quad \text{(phase speed)}. \tag{1.5}$$

1.3 Types of Waves

In order to make the above material more concrete, we now examine the characteristics of various types of waves which may be observed in the real world.

1.3.1 Ocean Surface Waves

These waves are manifested as undulations of the ocean surface as seen in figure 1.3. The speed of ocean waves is given by the formula

$$c = \left(\frac{g \tanh(kH)}{k} \right)^{1/2}, \tag{1.6}$$

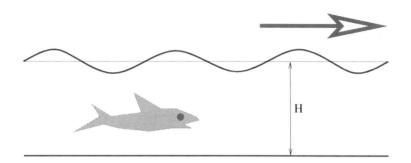

Figure 1.3: Wave on an ocean of depth H. The wave is moving to the right and the particles of water at the surface oscillate in elliptical trajectories as the wave crests and troughs pass.

where $g = 9.8$ m s^{-2} is the earth's gravitational force per unit mass, H is the depth of the ocean, and the hyperbolic tangent is defined as[1]

$$\tanh(x) = \frac{\exp(x) - \exp(-x)}{\exp(x) + \exp(-x)}. \tag{1.7}$$

The equation for the speed of ocean waves comes from the theory for oscillations of a fluid surface in a gravitional field.

As figure 1.4 shows, for $|x| \ll 1$, we can approximate the hyperbolic tangent by $\tanh(x) \approx x$, while for $|x| \gg 1$ it is $+1$ for $x > 0$ and -1 for $x < 0$. This leads to two limits: Since $x = kH$, the *shallow water* limit, which occurs when $kH \ll 1$, yields a wave speed of

$$c \approx (gH)^{1/2}, \quad \text{(shallow water waves)}, \tag{1.8}$$

while the *deep water* limit, which occurs when $kH \gg 1$, yields

$$c \approx (g/k)^{1/2}, \quad \text{(deep water waves)}. \tag{1.9}$$

Notice that the speed of shallow water waves depends only on the depth of the water and on g. In other words, all shallow water waves move at the same speed. On the other hand, deep water waves of longer wavelength (and hence smaller wavenumber) move more rapidly than those with shorter

---

[1]The notation $\exp(x)$ is just another way of writing the exponential function e^x. We prefer this way because it is prettier when the function argument is complicated.

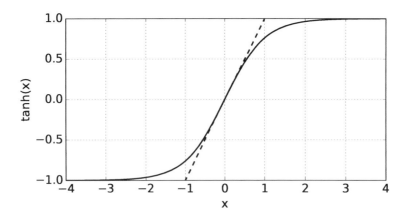

Figure 1.4: Plot of the function $\tanh(x)$. The dashed line shows our approximation $\tanh(x) \approx x$ for $|x| \ll 1$.

---

wavelength. Waves for which the wave speed varies with wavelength are called *dispersive*. Thus, deep water waves are dispersive, while shallow water waves are non-dispersive.

For water waves with wavelengths of a few centimeters or less, surface tension becomes important to the dynamics of the waves. In the deep water case, the wave speed at short wavelengths is given by the formula

$$c = (g/k + Ak)^{1/2} \tag{1.10}$$

where the constant A is related to an effect called surface tension. For an air-water interface near room temperature, $A \approx 74 \text{ cm}^3 \text{ s}^{-2}$.

1.3.2 Sound Waves

Sound is a longitudinal compression-expansion wave in a fluid. The wave speed for sound in an ideal gas is

$$c = (\gamma R T_{abs})^{1/2} \tag{1.11}$$

where γ and R are constants and T_{abs} is the *absolute temperature*. The absolute temperature is measured in Kelvins and is numerically given by

$$T_{abs} = T_C + 273° \tag{1.12}$$

where T_C is the temperature in Celsius degrees. The angular frequency of sound waves is thus given by

$$\omega = ck = (\gamma R T_{abs})^{1/2} k. \tag{1.13}$$

The speed of sound in air at normal temperatures is about 340 m s^{-1}.

1.3.3 Light

Light moves in a vacuum at a speed of $c_{vac} = 3 \times 10^8$ m s^{-1}. In transparent materials it moves at a speed less than c_{vac} by a factor n which is called the *refractive index* of the material:

$$c = c_{vac}/n. \tag{1.14}$$

Often the refractive index takes the form

$$n^2 \approx 1 + \frac{A}{1 - (k/k_R)^2}, \tag{1.15}$$

where k is the wavenumber and k_R and A are positive constants characteristic of the material. The angular frequency of light in a transparent medium is thus

$$\omega = kc = kc_{vac}/n. \tag{1.16}$$

1.4 Superposition Principle

It is found empirically that as long as the amplitudes of waves in most media are small, two waves in the same physical location don't interact with each other. Thus, for example, two waves moving in the opposite direction simply pass through each other without their shapes or amplitudes being changed. When collocated, the total wave displacement is just the sum of the displacements of the individual waves. This is called the *superposition principle*. At sufficiently large amplitude the superposition principle often breaks down — interacting waves may scatter off of each other, lose amplitude, or change their form.

Interference is a consequence of the superposition principle. When two or more waves are superimposed, the net wave displacement is just the algebraic sum of the displacements of the individual waves. Since these displacements

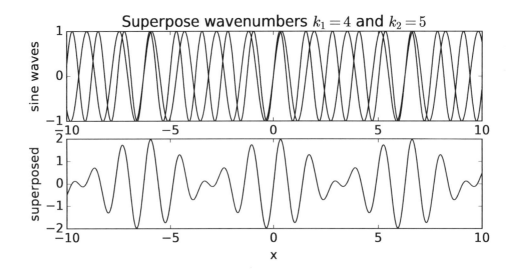

Figure 1.5: Superposition (lower panel) of two sine waves (shown individually in the upper panel) with equal amplitudes and wavenumbers $k_1 = 4$ and $k_2 = 5$.

can be positive or negative, the net displacement can either be greater or less than the individual wave displacements. The former case, which occurs when both displacements are of the same sign, is called *constructive interference*, while *destructive interference* occurs when they are of opposite sign.

Let us see what happens when we superimpose two sine waves with different wavenumbers. Figure 1.5 shows the superposition of two waves with wavenumbers $k_1 = 4$ and $k_2 = 5$. Notice that the result is a wave with about the same wavelength as the two initial waves, but which varies in amplitude depending on whether the two sine waves are interfering constructively or destructively. We say that the waves are *in phase* if they are interfering constructively, and they are *out of phase* if they are interfering destructively.

What happens when the wavenumbers of the two sine waves are changed? Figure 1.6 shows the result when $k_1 = 10$ and $k_2 = 11$. Notice that though the wavelength of the resultant wave is decreased, the locations where the amplitude is maximum have the same separation in x as in figure 1.5.

If we superimpose waves with $k_1 = 10$ and $k_2 = 12$, as is shown in figure 1.7, we see that the x spacing of the regions of maximum amplitude has

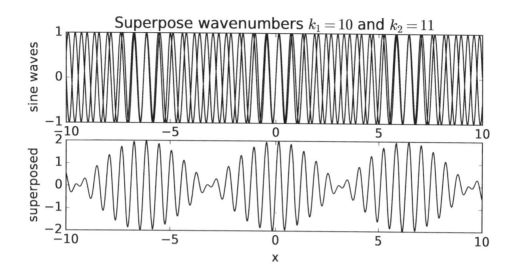

Figure 1.6: Superposition of two sine waves with equal amplitudes and wavenumbers $k_1 = 10$ and $k_2 = 11$.

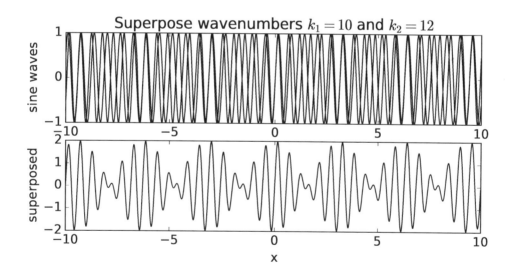

Figure 1.7: Superposition of two sine waves with equal amplitudes and wavenumbers $k_1 = 10$ and $k_2 = 12$.

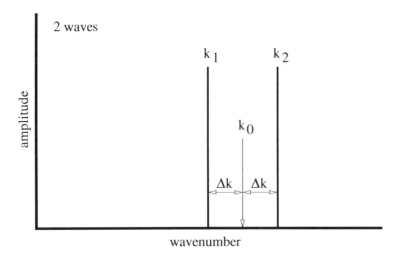

Figure 1.8: Representation of the wavenumbers and amplitudes of two superimposed sine waves.

decreased by a factor of two. Thus, while the wavenumber of the resultant wave seems to be related to something like the *average* of the wavenumbers of the component waves, the spacing between regions of maximum wave amplitude appears to go inversely with the *difference* of the wavenumbers of the component waves. In other words, if k_1 and k_2 are close together, the amplitude maxima are far apart and vice versa.

We can symbolically represent the sine waves that make up figures 1.5, 1.6, and 1.7 by a plot such as that shown in figure 1.8. The amplitudes and wavenumbers of each of the sine waves are indicated by vertical lines in this figure.

The regions of large wave amplitude are called *wave packets*. Wave packets will play a central role in what is to follow, so it is important that we acquire a good understanding of them. The wave packets produced by only two sine waves are not well separated along the x-axis. However, if we superimpose many waves, we can produce an isolated wave packet. For example, figure 1.9 shows the results of superimposing 20 sine waves with wavenumbers $k = 0.4m$, $m = 1, 2, \ldots, 20$, where the amplitudes of the waves are largest for wavenumbers near $k = 4$. In particular, we assume that the amplitude of each sine wave is proportional to $\exp[-(k - k_0)^2/\Delta k^2]$, where $k_0 = 4$ defines

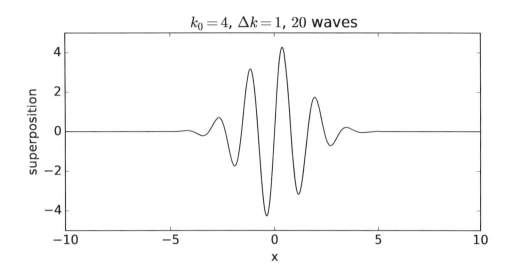

Figure 1.9: Superposition of twenty sine waves with $k_0 = 4$ and $\Delta k = 1$.

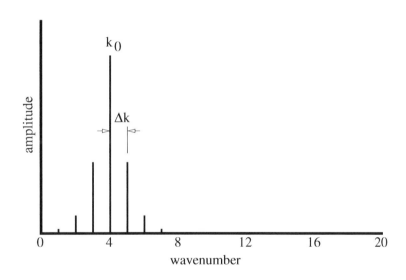

Figure 1.10: Representation of the distribution of wavenumbers and amplitudes of 20 superimposed sine waves with maximum at $k_0 = 4$ and half-width $\Delta k = 1$.

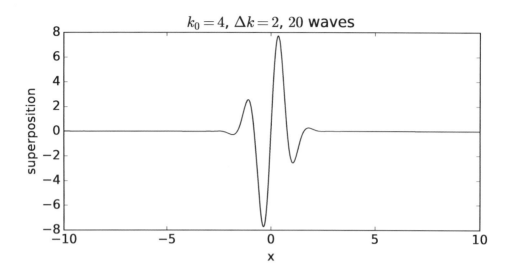

Figure 1.11: Superposition of twenty sine waves with $k_0 = 4$ and $\Delta k = 2$.

the maximum of the distribution of wavenumbers and $\Delta k = 1$ defines the half-width of this distribution. The amplitudes of each of the sine waves making up the wave packet in figure 1.9 are shown schematically in figure 1.10.

The quantity Δk controls the distribution of the sine waves being superimposed — only those waves with a wavenumber k within approximately Δk of the *central wavenumber* k_0 of the wave packet, i. e., for $3 \le k \le 5$ in this case, contribute significantly to the sum. If Δk is changed to 2, so that wavenumbers in the range $2 \le k \le 6$ contribute significantly, the wavepacket becomes narrower, as is shown in figures 1.11 and 1.12. Δk is called the *wavenumber spread* of the wave packet, and it evidently plays a role similar to the difference in wavenumbers in the superposition of two sine waves — the larger the wavenumber spread, the smaller the physical size of the wave packet. Furthermore, the wavenumber of the oscillations within the wave packet is given approximately by the central wavenumber.

We can better understand how wave packets work by mathematically analyzing the simple case of the superposition of two sine waves. Let us define $k_0 = (k_1 + k_2)/2$ where k_1 and k_2 are the wavenumbers of the component waves. Furthermore let us set $\Delta k = (k_2 - k_1)/2$. The quantities k_0 and Δk

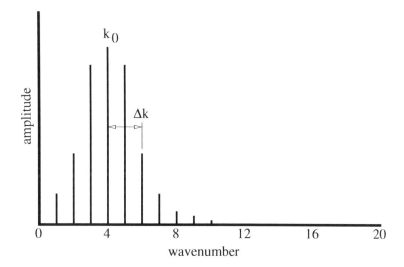

Figure 1.12: Representation of the distribution of wavenumbers and amplitudes of 20 superimposed sine waves with maximum at $k_0 = 4$ and half-width $\Delta k = 2$.

are graphically illustrated in figure 1.8. We can write $k_1 = k_0 - \Delta k$ and $k_2 = k_0 + \Delta k$ and use the trigonometric identity $\sin(a + b) = \sin(a)\cos(b) + \cos(a)\sin(b)$ to find

$$
\begin{aligned}
\sin(k_1 x) + \sin(k_2 x) &= \sin[(k_0 - \Delta k)x] + \sin[(k_0 + \Delta k)x] \\
&= \sin(k_0 x)\cos(\Delta k x) - \cos(k_0 x)\sin(\Delta k x) + \\
&\quad \sin(k_0 x)\cos(\Delta k x) + \cos(k_0 x)\sin(\Delta k x) \\
&= 2\sin(k_0 x)\cos(\Delta k x).
\end{aligned}
\tag{1.17}
$$

The sine factor on the bottom line of the above equation produces the oscillations within the wave packet, and as speculated earlier, this oscillation has a wavenumber k_0 equal to the average of the wavenumbers of the component waves. The cosine factor modulates this wave with a spacing between regions of maximum amplitude of

$$
\Delta x = \pi/\Delta k.
\tag{1.18}
$$

Thus, as we observed in the earlier examples, the length of the wave packet Δx is inversely related to the spread of the wavenumbers Δk (which in this case is just the difference between the two wavenumbers) of the component waves. This relationship is central to the uncertainty principle of quantum mechanics.

1.5   Beats

Suppose two sound waves of different frequency but equal amplitude impinge on your ear at the same time. The displacement perceived by your ear is the superposition of these two waves, with time dependence

$$h(t) = \sin(\omega_1 t) + \sin(\omega_2 t) = 2\sin(\omega_0 t)\cos(\Delta\omega t), \tag{1.19}$$

where we have used the above math trick, and where $\omega_0 = (\omega_1 + \omega_2)/2$ and $\Delta\omega = (\omega_2 - \omega_1)/2$. What you actually hear is a tone with angular frequency ω_0 which fades in and out with period

$$T_{beat} = \pi/|\Delta\omega| = 2\pi/|\omega_2 - \omega_1| = 1/|f_2 - f_1|. \tag{1.20}$$

The *beat frequency* is simply

$$f_{beat} = 1/T_{beat} = |f_2 - f_1|. \tag{1.21}$$

Note how beats are the time analog of wave packets — the mathematics are the same except that frequency replaces wavenumber and time replaces space.

1.6   Interferometers

An interferometer is a device which splits a beam of light (or other wave) into two sub-beams, shifts the phase of one sub-beam with respect to the other, and then superimposes the sub-beams so that they interfere constructively or destructively, depending on the magnitude of the phase shift between them. In this section we study the Michelson interferometer and interferometric effects in thin films.

1.6.1   The Michelson Interferometer

The American physicist Albert Michelson invented the optical interferometer illustrated in figure 1.13. The incoming beam is split into two beams by

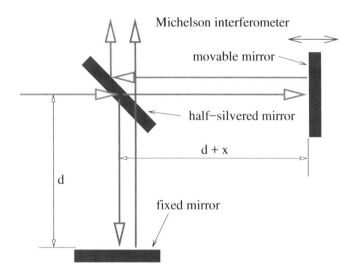

Figure 1.13: Sketch of a Michelson interferometer.

the half-silvered mirror. Each sub-beam reflects off of another mirror which returns it to the half-silvered mirror, where the two sub-beams recombine as shown. One of the reflecting mirrors is movable by a sensitive micrometer device, allowing the path length of the corresponding sub-beam, and hence the phase relationship between the two sub-beams, to be altered. As figure 1.13 shows, the difference in path length between the two sub-beams is $2x$ because the horizontal sub-beam traverses the path twice. Thus, constructive interference occurs when this path difference is an integral number of wavelengths, i. e.,

$$2x = m\lambda, \quad m = 0, \pm 1, \pm 2, \ldots \quad \text{(Michelson interferometer)} \qquad (1.22)$$

where λ is the wavelength of the wave and m is an integer. Note that m is the number of wavelengths that fits evenly into the distance $2x$.

1.7   Thin Films

One of the most revealing examples of interference occurs when light interacts with a thin film of transparent material such as a soap bubble. Figure 1.14 shows how a plane wave normally incident on the film is partially reflected

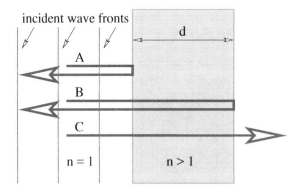

Figure 1.14: Plane light wave normally incident on a transparent thin film of thickness d and index of refraction $n > 1$. Partial reflection occurs at the front surface of the film, resulting in beam A, and at the rear surface, resulting in beam B. Much of the wave passes completely through the film, as with C.

by the front and rear surfaces. The waves reflected off the front and rear surfaces of the film interfere with each other. The interference can be either constructive or destructive depending on the phase difference between the two reflected waves.

If the wavelength of the incoming wave is λ, one would naively expect constructive interference to occur between the A and B beams if $2d$ were an integral multiple of λ.

Two factors complicate this picture. First, the wavelength inside the film is *not* λ, but λ/n, where n is the index of refraction of the film. Constructive interference would then occur if $2d = m\lambda/n$. Second, it turns out that an additional phase shift of half a wavelength occurs upon reflection when the wave is incident on material with a higher index of refraction than the medium in which the incident beam is immersed. This phase shift doesn't occur when light is reflected from a region with lower index of refraction than felt by the incident beam. Thus beam B doesn't acquire any additional phase shift upon reflection. As a consequence, constructive interference actually occurs when

$$2d = (m + 1/2)\lambda/n, \quad m = 0, 1, 2, \ldots \quad \text{(constructive interference)} \quad (1.23)$$

while destructive interference results when

$$2d = m\lambda/n, \quad m = 0, 1, 2, \ldots \quad \text{(destructive interference)}. \qquad (1.24)$$

When we look at a soap bubble, we see bands of colors reflected back from a light source. What is the origin of these bands? Light from ordinary sources is generally a mixture of wavelengths ranging from roughly $\lambda = 4.5 \times 10^{-7}$ m (violet light) to $\lambda = 6.5 \times 10^{-7}$ m (red light). In between violet and red we also have blue, green, and yellow light, in that order. Because of the different wavelengths associated with different colors, it is clear that for a mixed light source we will have some colors interfering constructively while others interfere destructively. Those undergoing constructive interference will be visible in reflection, while those undergoing destructive interference will not.

Another factor enters as well. If the light is not normally incident on the film, the difference in the distances traveled between beams reflected off of the front and rear faces of the film will not be just twice the thickness of the film. To understand this case quantitatively, we need the concept of refraction, which will be developed later in the context of geometrical optics. However, it should be clear that different wavelengths will undergo constructive interference for different angles of incidence of the incoming light. Different portions of the thin film will in general be viewed at different angles, and will therefore exhibit different colors under reflection, resulting in the colorful patterns normally seen in soap bubbles.

1.8 Math Review — Derivatives

This section provides a quick review of the idea of the derivative. Often we are interested in the slope of a line tangent to a function $y(x)$ at some value of x. This slope is called the *derivative* and is denoted dy/dx. Since a tangent line to the function can be defined at any point x, the derivative itself is a function of x:

$$g(x) = \frac{dy(x)}{dx}. \qquad (1.25)$$

As figure 1.15 illustrates, the slope of the tangent line at some point on the function may be approximated by the slope of a line connecting two points, A and B, set a finite distance apart on the curve:

$$\frac{dy}{dx} \approx \frac{\Delta y}{\Delta x}. \qquad (1.26)$$

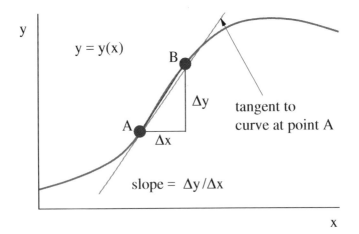

Figure 1.15: Estimation of the derivative, which is the slope of the tangent line. When point B approaches point A, the slope of the line AB approaches the slope of the tangent to the curve at point A.

As B is moved closer to A, the approximation becomes better. In the limit when B moves infinitely close to A, it is exact.

Derivatives of some common functions are now given. In each case a is a constant.

$$\frac{dx^a}{dx} = ax^{a-1} \tag{1.27}$$

$$\frac{d}{dx}\exp(ax) = a\exp(ax) \tag{1.28}$$

$$\frac{d}{dx}\log(ax) = \frac{1}{x} \tag{1.29}$$

$$\frac{d}{dx}\sin(ax) = a\cos(ax) \tag{1.30}$$

$$\frac{d}{dx}\cos(ax) = -a\sin(ax) \tag{1.31}$$

$$\frac{da f(x)}{dx} = a\frac{df(x)}{dx} \tag{1.32}$$

$$\frac{d}{dx}[f(x) + g(x)] = \frac{df(x)}{dx} + \frac{dg(x)}{dx} \tag{1.33}$$

$$\frac{d}{dx}f(x)g(x) = \frac{df(x)}{dx}g(x) + f(x)\frac{dg(x)}{dx} \quad \text{(product rule)} \quad (1.34)$$

$$\frac{d}{dx}f(y) = \frac{df}{dy}\frac{dy}{dx} \quad \text{(chain rule)} \quad (1.35)$$

The product and chain rules are used to compute the derivatives of complex functions. For instance,

$$\frac{d}{dx}(\sin(x)\cos(x)) = \frac{d\sin(x)}{dx}\cos(x) + \sin(x)\frac{d\cos(x)}{dx} = \cos^2(x) - \sin^2(x)$$

and

$$\frac{d}{dx}\log(\sin(x)) = \frac{1}{\sin(x)}\frac{d\sin(x)}{dx} = \frac{\cos(x)}{\sin(x)}.$$

1.9   Group Velocity

We now ask the following question: How fast do wave packets move? Surprisingly, we often find that wave packets move at a speed very different from the phase speed, $c = \omega/k$, of the wave composing the wave packet.

We shall find that the speed of motion of wave packets, referred to as the *group velocity*, is given by

$$u = \left.\frac{d\omega}{dk}\right|_{k=k_0} \quad \text{(group velocity).} \quad (1.36)$$

The derivative of $\omega(k)$ with respect to k is first computed and then evaluated at $k = k_0$, the central wavenumber of the wave packet of interest.

The relationship between the angular frequency and the wavenumber for a wave, $\omega = \omega(k)$, depends on the type of wave being considered. Whatever this relationship turns out to be in a particular case, it is called the *dispersion relation* for the type of wave in question.

As an example of a group velocity calculation, suppose we want to find the velocity of deep ocean wave packets for a central wavelength of $\lambda_0 = 60$ m. This corresponds to a central wavenumber of $k_0 = 2\pi/\lambda_0 \approx 0.1$ m^{-1}. The phase speed of deep ocean waves is $c = (g/k)^{1/2}$. However, since $c \equiv \omega/k$, we find the frequency of deep ocean waves to be $\omega = (gk)^{1/2}$. The group velocity is therefore $u \equiv d\omega/dk = (g/k)^{1/2}/2 = c/2$. For the specified central wavenumber, we find that $u \approx (9.8 \text{ m s}^{-2}/0.1 \text{ m}^{-1})^{1/2}/2 \approx 5 \text{ m s}^{-1}$. By

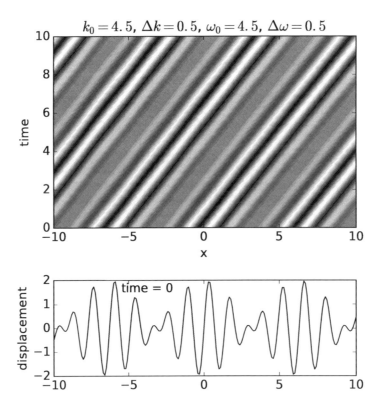

Figure 1.16: Upper panel: Net displacement of the sum of two traveling sine waves plotted in the $x - t$ plane. The white indicates where the displacement is large and positive, while the black indicates where it is large and negative. Non-dispersive case with $u_p = u_g = 1$.. Lower panel: Plot of wave displacement as a function of x at time $t = 0$.

contrast, the phase speed of deep ocean waves with this wavelength is $c \approx 10$ m s^{-1}.

Dispersive waves are waves in which the phase speed varies with wavenumber. It is easy to show that dispersive waves have unequal phase and group velocities, while these velocities are equal for non-dispersive waves.

1.9.1 Derivation of Group Velocity Formula

We now derive equation (1.36). It is easiest to do this for the simplest wave packets, namely those constructed out of the superposition of just two sine waves. We will proceed by adding two waves with full space and time dependence:

$$h = \sin(k_1 x - \omega_1 t) + \sin(k_2 x - \omega_2 t) \qquad (1.37)$$

After algebraic and trigonometric manipulations familiar from earlier sections, we find

$$h = 2\sin(k_0 x - \omega_0 t)\cos(\Delta k x - \Delta \omega t), \qquad (1.38)$$

where as before we have $k_0 = (k_1 + k_2)/2$, $\omega_0 = (\omega_1 + \omega_2)/2$, $\Delta k = (k_2 - k_1)/2$, and $\Delta \omega = (\omega_2 - \omega_1)/2$.

Again think of this as a sine wave of frequency ω_0 and wavenumber k_0 modulated by a cosine function. In this case the modulation pattern moves with a speed so as to keep the argument of the cosine function constant:

$$\Delta k x - \Delta \omega t = const. \qquad (1.39)$$

Differentiating this with respect to t while holding Δk and $\Delta \omega$ constant yields

$$u \equiv \frac{dx}{dt} = \frac{\Delta \omega}{\Delta k}. \qquad (1.40)$$

In the limit in which the deltas become very small, this reduces to the derivative

$$u = \frac{d\omega}{dk}, \qquad (1.41)$$

which is the desired result.

1.9.2 Examples

We now illustrate some examples of phase speed and group velocity by showing the displacement resulting from the superposition of two sine waves, as given by equation (1.38), in the $x - t$ plane. This is an example of a spacetime diagram, of which we will see many examples later on.

The upper panel of figure 1.16 shows a non-dispersive case in which the phase speed equals the group velocity. The white and black regions indicate respectively strong wave crests and troughs (i. e., regions of large positive and negative displacements), with grays indicating a displacement near zero.

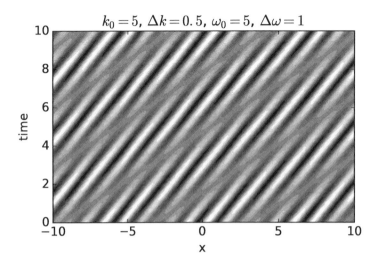

Figure 1.17: As in the upper panel of figure 1.16 except a dispersive case with $u_p = 1$, $u_g = 2$.

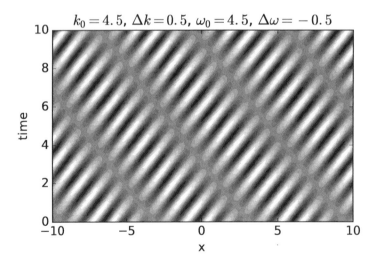

Figure 1.18: As in the upper panel of figure 1.16 except a dispersive case with phase and group velocities in opposite directions, $u_p = 1$, $u_g = -1$.

Regions with large displacements indicate the location of wave packets. The positions of waves and wave packets at any given time may therefore be determined by drawing a horizontal line across the graph at the desired time and examining the variations in wave displacement along this line. The lower panel of this figure shows the wave displacement as a function of x at time $t = 0$ as an aid to interpretation of the upper panel.

Notice that as time increases, the crests move to the right. This corresponds to the motion of the waves within the wave packets. Note also that the wave packets, i. e., the broad regions of large positive and negative amplitudes, move to the right with increasing time as well.

Since velocity is distance moved Δx divided by elapsed time Δt, the slope of a line in figure 1.16, $\Delta t / \Delta x$, is one over the velocity of whatever that line represents. The slopes of lines representing crests are the same as the slopes of lines representing wave packets in this case, which indicates that the two move at the same velocity. Since the speed of movement of wave crests is the phase speed and the speed of movement of wave packets is the group velocity, the two velocities are equal and the non-dispersive nature of this case is confirmed.

Figure 1.17 shows a dispersive wave in which the group velocity is twice the phase speed, while figure 1.18 shows a case in which the group velocity is actually opposite in sign to the phase speed. See if you can confirm that the phase and group velocities seen in each figure correspond to the values for these quantities calculated from the specified frequencies and wavenumbers.

1.10   Problems

1. Measure your pulse rate. Compute the ordinary frequency of your heart beat in cycles per second. Compute the angular frequency in radians per second. Compute the period.

2. An important wavelength for radio waves in radio astronomy is 21 cm. (This comes from neutral hydrogen.) Compute the wavenumber of this wave. Compute the ordinary and angular frequencies. (The speed of light is 3×10^8 m s^{-1}.)

3. Sketch the resultant wave obtained from superimposing the waves $A = \sin(2x)$ and $B = \sin(3x)$. By using the trigonometric identity given in equation (1.17), obtain a formula for $A + B$ in terms of $\sin(5x/2)$ and

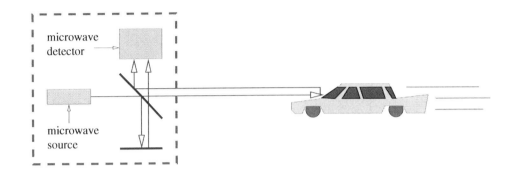

Figure 1.19: Sketch of a police radar.

$\cos(x/2)$. Does the wave obtained from sketching this formula agree with your earlier sketch?

4. Two sine waves with wavelengths λ_1 and λ_2 are superimposed, making wave packets of length L. If we wish to make L larger, should we make λ_1 and λ_2 closer together or farther apart? Explain your reasoning.

5. By examining figure 1.9 versus figure 1.10 and then figure 1.11 versus figure 1.12, determine whether equation (1.18) works at least in an approximate sense for isolated wave packets.

6. The frequencies of the chromatic scale in music are given by

$$f_i = f_0 2^{i/12}, \quad i = 0, 1, 2, \ldots, 11, \tag{1.42}$$

where f_0 is a constant equal to the frequency of the lowest note in the scale.

(a) Compute f_1 through f_{11} if $f_0 = 440$ Hz (the "A" note).

(b) Using the above results, what is the beat frequency between the "A" ($i = 0$) and "B" ($i = 2$) notes? (The frequencies are given here in cycles per second rather than radians per second.)

(c) Which pair of the above frequencies $f_0 - f_{11}$ yields the smallest beat frequency? Explain your reasoning.

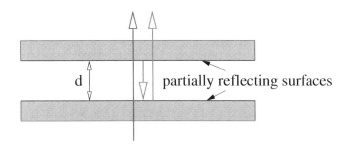

Figure 1.20: Sketch of a Fabry-Perot interferometer.

7. Large ships in general cannot move faster than the phase speed of surface waves with a wavelength equal to twice the ship's length. This is because most of the propulsive force goes into making big waves under these conditions rather than accelerating the ship.

   (a) How fast can a 300 m long ship move in very deep water?

   (b) As the ship moves into shallow water, does its maximum speed increase or decrease? Explain.

8. Given the formula for refractive index of light quoted in this section, for what range of k does the phase speed of light in a transparent material take on real values which exceed the speed of light in a vacuum?

9. A police radar works by splitting a beam of microwaves, part of which is reflected back to the radar from your car where it is made to interfere with the other part which travels a fixed path, as shown in figure 1.19.

   (a) If the wavelength of the microwaves is λ, how far do you have to travel in your car for the interference between the two beams to go from constructive to destructive to constructive?

   (b) If you are traveling toward the radar at speed $v = 30$ m s^{-1}, use the above result to determine the number of times per second constructive interference peaks will occur. Assume that $\lambda = 3$ cm.

10. Suppose you know the wavelength of light passing through a Michelson interferometer with high accuracy. Describe how you could use the interferometer to measure the length of a small piece of material.

11. A Fabry-Perot interferometer (see figure 1.20) consists of two parallel half-silvered mirrors placed a distance d from each other as shown. The beam passing straight through interferes with the beam which reflects once off of both of the mirrored surfaces as shown. For wavelength λ, what values of d result in constructive interference?

12. A Fabry-Perot interferometer has spacing $d = 2$ cm between the glass plates, causing the direct and doubly reflected beams to interfere (see figure 1.20). As air is pumped out of the gap between the plates, the beams go through 23 cycles of constructive-destructive-constructive interference. If the wavelength of the light in the interfering beams is 5×10^{-7} m, determine the index of refraction of the air initially in the interferometer.

13. Measurements on a certain kind of wave reveal that the angular frequency of the wave varies with wavenumber as shown in the following table:

ω (s^{-1})	k (m^{-1})
5	1
20	2
45	3
80	4
125	5

(a) Compute the phase speed of the wave for $k = 3$ m^{-1} and for $k = 4$ m^{-1}.

(b) Estimate the group velocity for $k = 3.5$ m^{-1} using a finite difference approximation to the derivative.

14. Suppose some type of wave has the (admittedly weird) dispersion relation shown in figure 1.21.

(a) For what values of k is the phase speed of the wave positive?

(b) For what values of k is the group velocity positive?

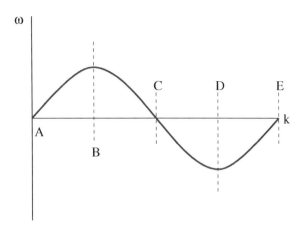

Figure 1.21: Sketch of a weird dispersion relation.

15. Group velocities of various waves.

    (a) Compute the group velocity for shallow water waves. Compare it with the phase speed of shallow water waves. (Hint: You first need to derive a formula for $\omega(k)$ from $c(k)$.)

    (b) Repeat the above problem for deep water waves.

    (c) Repeat for sound waves. What does this case have in common with shallow water waves?

Chapter 2

Waves in Two and Three Dimensions

In this chapter we extend the ideas of the previous chapter to the case of waves in more than one dimension. The extension of the sine wave to higher dimensions is the *plane wave*. Wave packets in two and three dimensions arise when plane waves moving in different directions are superimposed.

Diffraction results from the disruption of a wave which is impingent upon an object. Those parts of the wave front hitting the object are scattered, modified, or destroyed. The resulting *diffraction pattern* comes from the subsequent interference of the various pieces of the modified wave. A knowledge of diffraction is necessary to understand the behavior and limitations of optical instruments such as telescopes.

Diffraction and interference in two and three dimensions can be manipulated to produce useful devices such as the *diffraction grating*.

2.1 Math Tutorial — Vectors

Before we can proceed further we need to explore the idea of a *vector*. A vector is a quantity which expresses both magnitude and direction. Graphically we represent a vector as an arrow. In typeset notation a vector is represented by a boldface character, while in handwriting an arrow is drawn over the character representing the vector.

Figure 2.1 shows some examples of *displacement vectors*, i. e., vectors which represent the displacement of one object from another, and introduces

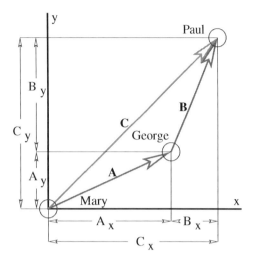

Figure 2.1: Displacement vectors in a plane. Vector **A** represents the displacement of George from Mary, while vector **B** represents the displacement of Paul from George. Vector **C** represents the displacement of Paul from Mary and $\mathbf{C} = \mathbf{A} + \mathbf{B}$. The quantities A_x, A_y, etc., represent the Cartesian components of the vectors.

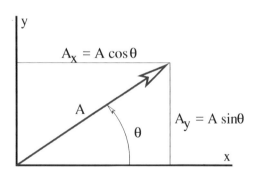

Figure 2.2: Definition sketch for the angle θ representing the orientation of a two dimensional vector.

the idea of vector addition. The tail of vector **B** is collocated with the head of vector **A**, and the vector which stretches from the tail of **A** to the head of **B** is the sum of **A** and **B**, called **C** in figure 2.1.

The quantities A_x, A_y, etc., represent the *Cartesian components* of the vectors in figure 2.1. A vector can be represented either by its Cartesian components, which are just the projections of the vector onto the Cartesian coordinate axes, or by its direction and magnitude. The direction of a vector in two dimensions is generally represented by the counterclockwise angle of the vector relative to the x axis, as shown in figure 2.2. Conversion from one form to the other is given by the equations

$$A = (A_x^2 + A_y^2)^{1/2} \quad \theta = \tan^{-1}(A_y/A_x), \tag{2.1}$$

$$A_x = A\cos(\theta) \quad A_y = A\sin(\theta), \tag{2.2}$$

where A is the magnitude of the vector. A vector magnitude is sometimes represented by absolute value notation: $A \equiv |\mathbf{A}|$.

Notice that the inverse tangent gives a result which is ambiguous relative to adding or subtracting integer multiples of π. Thus the quadrant in which the angle lies must be resolved by independently examining the signs of A_x and A_y and choosing the appropriate value of θ.

To add two vectors, **A** and **B**, it is easiest to convert them to Cartesian component form. The components of the sum $\mathbf{C} = \mathbf{A} + \mathbf{B}$ are then just the sums of the components:

$$C_x = A_x + B_x \quad C_y = A_y + B_y. \tag{2.3}$$

Subtraction of vectors is done similarly, e. g., if $\mathbf{A} = \mathbf{C} - \mathbf{B}$, then

$$A_x = C_x - B_x \quad A_y = C_y - B_y. \tag{2.4}$$

A *unit vector* is a vector of unit length. One can always construct a unit vector from an ordinary (non-zero) vector by dividing the vector by its length: $\mathbf{n} = \mathbf{A}/|\mathbf{A}|$. This division operation is carried out by dividing each of the vector components by the number in the denominator. Alternatively, if the vector is expressed in terms of length and direction, the magnitude of the vector is divided by the denominator and the direction is unchanged.

Unit vectors can be used to define a Cartesian coordinate system. Conventionally, **i**, **j**, and **k** indicate the x, y, and z axes of such a system. Note that **i**, **j**, and **k** are mutually perpendicular. Any vector can be represented in terms

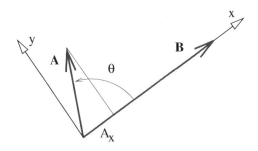

Figure 2.3: Definition sketch for dot product.

of unit vectors and its Cartesian components: $\mathbf{A} = A_x\mathbf{i} + A_y\mathbf{j} + A_z\mathbf{k}$. An alternate way to represent a vector is as a list of components: $\mathbf{A} = (A_x, A_y, A_z)$. We tend to use the latter representation since it is somewhat more economical notation.

There are two ways to multiply two vectors, yielding respectively what are known as the *dot product* and the *cross product*. The cross product yields another vector while the dot product yields a number. Here we will discuss only the dot product. The cross product will be presented later when it is needed.

Given vectors $\mathbf{A}$ and $\mathbf{B}$, the dot product of the two is defined as

$$\mathbf{A} \cdot \mathbf{B} \equiv |\mathbf{A}||\mathbf{B}|\cos\theta, \qquad (2.5)$$

where θ is the angle between the two vectors. In two dimensions an alternate expression for the dot product exists in terms of the Cartesian components of the vectors:

$$\mathbf{A} \cdot \mathbf{B} = A_x B_x + A_y B_y. \qquad (2.6)$$

It is easy to show that this is equivalent to the cosine form of the dot product when the x axis lies along one of the vectors, as in figure 2.3. Notice in particular that $A_x = |\mathbf{A}|\cos\theta$, while $B_x = |\mathbf{B}|$ and $B_y = 0$. Thus, $\mathbf{A} \cdot \mathbf{B} = |\mathbf{A}|\cos\theta|\mathbf{B}|$ in this case, which is identical to the form given in equation (2.5).

All that remains to be proven for equation (2.6) to hold in general is to show that it yields the same answer regardless of how the Cartesian coordinate system is oriented relative to the vectors. To do this, we must show that $A_x B_x + A_y B_y = A_x' B_x' + A_y' B_y'$, where the primes indicate components in a coordinate system rotated from the original coordinate system.

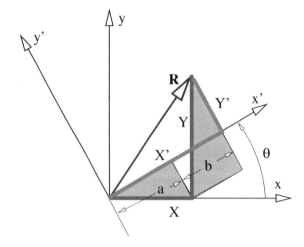

Figure 2.4: Definition figure for rotated coordinate system. The vector $\mathbf{R}$ has components X and Y in the unprimed coordinate system and components X' and Y' in the primed coordinate system.

Figure 2.4 shows the vector $\mathbf{R}$ resolved in two coordinate systems rotated with respect to each other. From this figure it is clear that $X' = a + b$. Focusing on the shaded triangles, we see that $a = X \cos \theta$ and $b = Y \sin \theta$. Thus, we find $X' = X \cos \theta + Y \sin \theta$. Similar reasoning shows that $Y' = -X \sin \theta + Y \cos \theta$. Substituting these and using the trigonometric identity $\cos^2 \theta + \sin^2 \theta = 1$ results in

$$
\begin{aligned}
A'_x B'_x + A'_y B'_y &= (A_x \cos \theta + A_y \sin \theta)(B_x \cos \theta + B_y \sin \theta) \\
&+ (-A_x \sin \theta + A_y \cos \theta)(-B_x \sin \theta + B_y \cos \theta) \\
&= A_x B_x + A_y B_y
\end{aligned}
\tag{2.7}
$$

thus proving the complete equivalence of the two forms of the dot product as given by equations (2.5) and (2.6). Multiply out the above expression to verify this.

A numerical quantity that doesn't depend on which coordinate system is being used is called a *scalar*. The dot product of two vectors is a scalar. However, the components of a vector, taken individually, are not scalars, since the components change as the coordinate system changes. Since the laws of physics cannot depend on the choice of coordinate system being used,

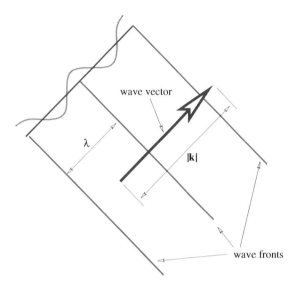

Figure 2.5: Definition sketch for a plane sine wave in two dimensions. The wave fronts are constant phase surfaces separated by one wavelength. The wave vector is normal to the wave fronts and its length is the wavenumber.

---

we insist that physical laws be expressed in terms of scalars and vectors, but not in terms of the components of vectors.

In three dimensions the cosine form of the dot product remains the same, while the component form is

$$\mathbf{A} \cdot \mathbf{B} = A_x B_x + A_y B_y + A_z B_z. \tag{2.8}$$

2.2 Plane Waves

A plane wave in two or three dimensions is like a sine wave in one dimension except that crests and troughs aren't points, but form lines (2-D) or planes (3-D) perpendicular to the direction of wave propagation. Figure 2.5 shows a plane sine wave in two dimensions. The large arrow is a vector called the *wave vector*, which defines (1) the direction of wave propagation by its orientation perpendicular to the wave fronts, and (2) the wavenumber by its length. We can think of a wave front as a line along the crest of the wave. The equation for the displacement associated with a plane sine wave (of unit amplitude) in three dimensions at some instant in time is

$$h(x, y, z) = \sin(\mathbf{k} \cdot \mathbf{x}) = \sin(k_x x + k_y y + k_z z). \tag{2.9}$$

Since wave fronts are lines or surfaces of constant phase, the equation defining a wave front is simply $\mathbf{k} \cdot \mathbf{x} = const.$

In the two dimensional case we simply set $k_z = 0$. Therefore, a wave front, or line of constant phase ϕ in two dimensions is defined by the equation

$$\mathbf{k} \cdot \mathbf{x} = k_x x + k_y y = \phi \quad \text{(two dimensions).} \tag{2.10}$$

This can be easily solved for y to obtain the slope and intercept of the wave front in two dimensions.

As for one dimensional waves, the time evolution of the wave is obtained by adding a term $-\omega t$ to the phase of the wave. In three dimensions the wave displacement as a function of both space and time is given by

$$h(x, y, z, t) = \sin(k_x x + k_y y + k_z z - \omega t). \tag{2.11}$$

The frequency depends in general on all three components of the wave vector. The form of this function, $\omega = \omega(k_x, k_y, k_z)$, which as in the one dimensional case is called the *dispersion relation*, contains information about the physical behavior of the wave.

Some examples of dispersion relations for waves in two dimensions are as follows:

- Light waves in a vacuum in two dimensions obey

$$\omega = c(k_x^2 + k_y^2)^{1/2} \quad \text{(light),} \tag{2.12}$$

  where c is the speed of light in a vacuum.

- Deep water ocean waves in two dimensions obey

$$\omega = g^{1/2}(k_x^2 + k_y^2)^{1/4} \quad \text{(ocean waves),} \tag{2.13}$$

  where g is the strength of the Earth's gravitational field as before.

- Certain kinds of atmospheric waves confined to a vertical $x - z$ plane called *gravity waves* (not to be confused with the gravitational waves

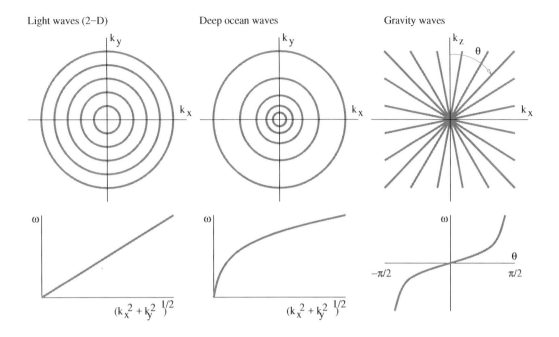

Figure 2.6: Contour plots of the dispersion relations for three kinds of waves in two dimensions. In the upper panels the curves show lines or contours along which the frequency ω takes on constant values. Contours are drawn for equally spaced values of ω. For light and ocean waves the frequency depends only on the magnitude of the wave vector, whereas for gravity waves it depends only on the wave vector's direction, as defined by the angle θ in the upper right panel. These dependences for each wave type are illustrated in the lower panels.

of general relativity)[1] obey

$$\omega = \frac{Nk_x}{k_z} \quad \text{(gravity waves)}, \qquad (2.14)$$

where N is a constant with the dimensions of inverse time called the Brunt-Väisälä frequency.

[1]Gravity waves in the atmosphere are vertical or slantwise oscillations of air parcels produced by buoyancy forces which push parcels back toward their original elevation after a vertical displacement.

Contour plots of these dispersion relations are plotted in the upper panels of figure 2.6. These plots are to be interpreted like topographic maps, where the lines represent contours of constant elevation. In the case of figure 2.6, constant values of frequency are represented instead. For simplicity, the actual values of frequency are not labeled on the contour plots, but are represented in the graphs in the lower panels. This is possible because frequency depends only on wave vector magnitude $(k_x^2 + k_y^2)^{1/2}$ for the first two examples, and only on wave vector direction θ for the third.

2.3   Superposition of Plane Waves

We now study wave packets in two dimensions by asking what the superposition of two plane sine waves looks like. If the two waves have different wavenumbers, but their wave vectors point in the same direction, the results are identical to those presented in the previous chapter, except that the wave packets are indefinitely elongated without change in form in the direction perpendicular to the wave vector. The wave packets produced in this case move in the direction of the wave vectors and thus appear to a stationary observer like a series of passing *pulses* with broad lateral extent.

Superimposing two plane waves which have the same frequency results in a stationary wave packet through which the individual wave fronts pass. This wave packet is also elongated indefinitely in some direction, but the direction of elongation depends on the dispersion relation for the waves being considered. These wave packets are in the form of steady *beams*, which guide the individual phase waves in some direction, but don't themselves change with time. By superimposing multiple plane waves, all with the same frequency, one can actually produce a single stationary beam, just as one can produce an isolated pulse by superimposing multiple waves with wave vectors pointing in the same direction.

If the frequency of a wave depends on the magnitude of the wave vector, but not on its direction, the wave's dispersion relation is called *isotropic*; otherwise it is *anisotropic*. In the isotropic case, two waves have the same frequency only if the lengths of their wave vectors, and hence their wavelengths, are the same. The first two examples in figure 2.6 satisfy this condition, while the last example is anisotropic.

We now use the language of vectors to investigate the superposition of

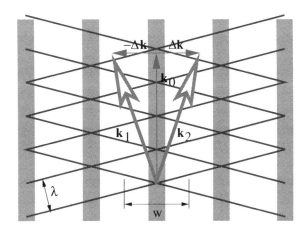

Figure 2.7: Wave fronts and wave vectors ($\mathbf{k}_1$ and $\mathbf{k}_2$) of two plane waves with the same wavelength but oriented in different directions. The vertical bands show regions of constructive interference where wave fronts coincide. The vertical regions in between have destructive interference, and hence define the lateral boundaries of the beams produced by the superposition. The quantities $\mathbf{k}_0$ and $\Delta\mathbf{k}$ are also shown.

two plane waves with wave vectors $\mathbf{k}_1$ and $\mathbf{k}_2$:

$$h = \sin(\mathbf{k}_1 \cdot \mathbf{x} - \omega t) + \sin(\mathbf{k}_2 \cdot \mathbf{x} - \omega t). \qquad (2.15)$$

Applying the trigonometric identity for the sine of the sum of two angles (as we have done previously), equation (2.15) can be reduced to

$$h = 2\sin(\mathbf{k}_0 \cdot \mathbf{x} - \omega t)\cos(\Delta\mathbf{k} \cdot x) \qquad (2.16)$$

where

$$\mathbf{k}_0 = (\mathbf{k}_1 + \mathbf{k}_2)/2 \quad \Delta\mathbf{k} = (\mathbf{k}_2 - \mathbf{k}_1)/2. \qquad (2.17)$$

This is in the form of a sine wave moving in the $\mathbf{k}_0$ direction with phase speed $c_{phase} = \omega/|\mathbf{k}_0|$ and wavenumber $|\mathbf{k}_0|$, modulated in the $\Delta\mathbf{k}$ direction by a cosine function. The lines of destructive interference are normal to $\Delta\mathbf{k}$. The distance w between lines of destructive interference is the distance between successive zeros of the cosine function in equation (2.16), implying that $|\Delta\mathbf{k}|w = \pi$, which leads to

$$w = \pi/|\Delta\mathbf{k}|. \qquad (2.18)$$

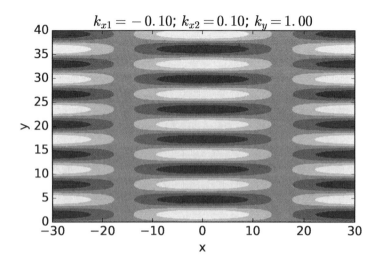

Figure 2.8: Example of beams produced by two plane waves with the same wavelength moving in different directions. The wave vectors of the two waves are $\mathbf{k} = (\pm 0.1, 1.0)$. Regions of positive displacement are lighter, while regions of negative displacement are darker.

Thus, the smaller $|\Delta \mathbf{k}|$, the greater is the beam diameter.

2.3.1 Two Waves of Identical Wavelength

In this section we investigate the beams produced by superimposing isotropic waves of the same frequency. Figure 2.7 illustrates what happens in such a superposition. Vectors $\mathbf{k}_1$ and $\mathbf{k}_2$ of equal length give rise to a mean wave vector $\mathbf{k}_0$ and half the difference, $\Delta \mathbf{k}$. As illustrated, the lines of constructive and destructive interference are perpendicular to $\Delta \mathbf{k}$. Figure 2.8 shows a concrete example of the beams produced by superposition of two plane waves of equal wavelength oriented as in figure 2.7. The beams are aligned vertically, since $\Delta \mathbf{k}$ is horizontal, with the lines of destructive interference separating the beams located near $x = \pm 16$. The transverse width of the beams of ≈ 32 satisfies equation (2.18) with $|\Delta \mathbf{k}| = 0.1$. Each beam is made up of vertically propagating phase waves, with the crests and troughs indicated by the regions of white and black.

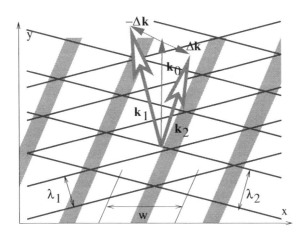

Figure 2.9: Wave fronts and wave vectors ($\mathbf{k}_1$ and $\mathbf{k}_2$) of two plane waves with different wavelengths oriented in different directions. The slanted bands show regions of constructive interference where wave fronts coincide. The slanted regions in between have destructive interference, and as mentioned previously, define the lateral limits of the beams produced by the superposition. The quantities $\mathbf{k}_0$ and $\Delta\mathbf{k}$ are also shown.

2.3.2   Two Waves of Differing Wavelength

In the third example of figure 2.6, the frequency of the wave depends only on the direction of the wave vector, independent of its magnitude, which is the reverse of the case for an isotropic dispersion relation. In this highly anisotropic case, different plane waves with the same frequency have wave vectors which point in the same direction, but have different lengths.

More generally, one might have waves for which the frequency depends on *both* the direction and magnitude of the wave vector. In this case, two different plane waves with the same frequency would typically have wave vectors which differ both in direction and magnitude. Such an example is illustrated in figures 2.9 and 2.10.

Figure 2.11 summarizes what we have learned about adding plane waves with the same frequency. In general, the beam orientation (and the lines of constructive interference) are not perpendicular to the wave fronts. This only occurs when the wave frequency is independent of wave vector direction.

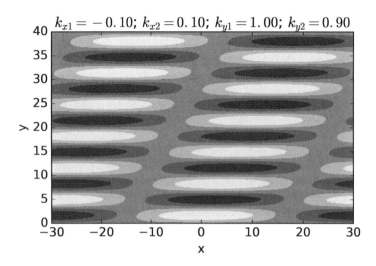

Figure 2.10: Example of beams produced by two plane waves with wave vectors differing in both direction and magnitude. The wave vectors of the two waves are $\mathbf{k}_1 = (-0.1, 1.0)$ and $\mathbf{k}_2 = (0.1, 0.9)$. Regions of positive displacement are lighter, while regions of negative displacement darker.

2.3.3   Many Waves with the Same Wavelength

As with wave packets in one dimension, we can add together more than two waves to produce an isolated wave packet. We will confine our attention here to the case of an isotropic dispersion relation in which all the wave vectors for a given frequency are of the same length.

Figure 2.12 shows an example of this in which wave vectors of the same wavelength but different directions are added together. Defining α_i as the angle of the ith wave vector clockwise from the vertical, as illustrated in figure 2.12, we could write the superposition of these waves at time $t = 0$ as

$$
\begin{aligned}
h &= \sum_i h_i \sin(k_{xi}x + k_{yi}y) \\
&= \sum_i h_i \sin[kx \sin(\alpha_i) + ky \cos(\alpha_i)] \qquad (2.19)
\end{aligned}
$$

where we have assumed that $k_{xi} = k \sin(\alpha_i)$ and $k_{yi} = k \cos(\alpha_i)$. The parameter $k = |\mathbf{k}|$ is the magnitude of the wave vector and is the same for all the

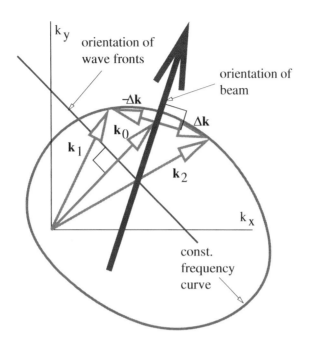

Figure 2.11: Illustration of factors entering the addition of two plane waves with the same frequency. The wave fronts are perpendicular to the vector average of the two wave vectors, $\mathbf{k}_0 = (\mathbf{k}_1 + \mathbf{k}_2)/2$, while the lines of constructive interference, which define the beam orientation, are oriented perpendicular to the difference between these two vectors, $\Delta\mathbf{k} = (\mathbf{k}_2 - \mathbf{k}_1)/2$.

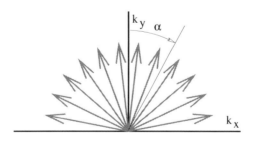

Figure 2.12: Illustration of wave vectors of plane waves which might be added together.

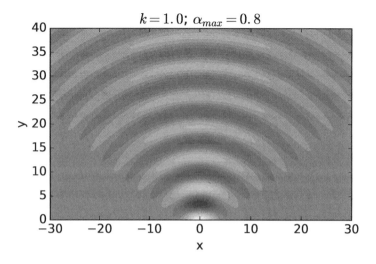

Figure 2.13: Plot of the displacement field $h(x, y)$ from equation (2.19) for $\alpha_{max} = 0.8$ and $k = 1$.

waves. Let us also assume in this example that the amplitude of each wave component decreases with increasing $|\alpha_i|$:

$$h_i = \exp[-(\alpha_i/\alpha_{max})^2]. \tag{2.20}$$

The exponential function decreases rapidly as its argument becomes more negative, and for practical purposes, only wave vectors with $|\alpha_i| \leq \alpha_{max}$ contribute significantly to the sum. We call α_{max} the *spreading angle*.

Figure 2.13 shows what $h(x, y)$ looks like when $\alpha_{max} = 0.8$ radians and $k = 1$. Notice that for $y = 0$ the wave amplitude is only large for a small region in the range $-4 < x < 4$. However, for $y > 0$ the wave spreads into a broad, semicircular pattern.

Figure 2.14 shows the computed pattern of $h(x, y)$ when the spreading angle $\alpha_{max} = 0.2$ radians. The wave amplitude is large for a much broader range of x at $y = 0$ in this case, roughly $-12 < x < 12$. On the other hand, the subsequent spread of the wave is much smaller than in the case of figure 2.13.

We conclude that a superposition of plane waves with wave vectors spread narrowly about a central wave vector which points in the y direction (as in

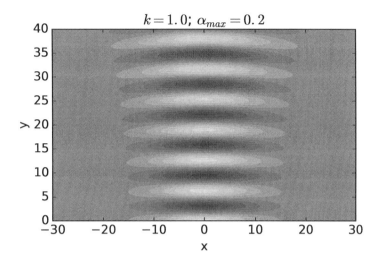

Figure 2.14: Plot of the displacement field $h(x, y)$ from equation (2.19) for $\alpha_{max} = 0.2$ and $k = 1$.

figure 2.14) produces a beam which is initially broad in x but for which the breadth increases only slightly with increasing y. However, a superposition of plane waves with wave vectors spread more broadly (as in figure 2.13) produces a beam which is initially narrow in x but which rapidly increases in width as y increases.

The relationship between the spreading angle α_{max} and the initial breadth of the beam is made more understandable by comparison with the results for the two-wave superposition discussed at the beginning of this section. As indicated by equation (2.18), large values of k_x, and hence α, are associated with small wave packet dimensions in the x direction and vice versa. The superposition of two waves doesn't capture the subsequent spread of the beam which occurs when many waves are superimposed, but it does lead to a rough quantitative relationship between α_{max} (which is just $\tan^{-1}(k_x/k_y)$ in the two wave case) and the initial breadth of the beam. If we invoke the small angle approximation for $\alpha = \alpha_{max}$ so that $\alpha_{max} = \tan^{-1}(k_x/k_y) \approx k_x/k_y \approx k_x/k$, then $k_x \approx k\alpha_{max}$ and equation (2.18) can be written $w = \pi/k_x \approx \pi/(k\alpha_{max}) = \lambda/(2\alpha_{max})$. Thus, we can find the approximate spreading angle

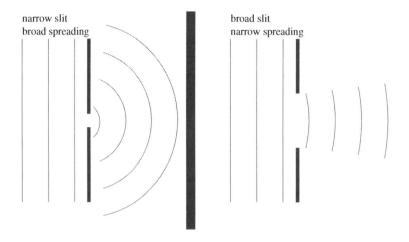

Figure 2.15: Schematic behavior when a plane wave impinges on a narrow slit and a broad slit.

from the wavelength of the wave λ and the initial breadth of the beam w:

$$\alpha_{max} \approx \lambda/(2w) \quad \text{(single slit spreading angle)}. \tag{2.21}$$

2.4   Diffraction Through a Single Slit

How does all of this apply to the passage of waves through a slit? Imagine a plane wave of wavelength λ impingent on a barrier with a slit. The barrier transforms the plane wave with infinite extent in the lateral direction into a beam with initial transverse dimensions equal to the width of the slit. The subsequent development of the beam is illustrated in figures 2.13 and 2.14, and schematically in figure 2.15. In particular, if the slit width is comparable to the wavelength, the beam spreads broadly as in figure 2.13. If the slit width is large compared to the wavelength, the beam doesn't spread as much, as figure 2.14 illustrates. Equation (2.21) gives us an approximate quantitative result for the spreading angle if w is interpreted as the width of the slit.

One use of the above equation is in determining the maximum angular resolution of optical instruments such as telescopes. The primary lens or mirror can be thought of as a rather large "slit". Light from a distant

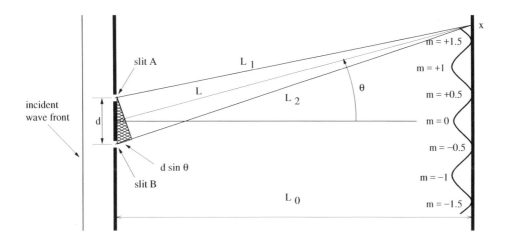

Figure 2.16: Definition sketch for the double slit. Light passing through slit B travels an extra distance to the screen equal to $d \sin \theta$ compared to light passing through slit A.

point source is essentially in the form of a plane wave when it arrives at the telescope. However, the light passed by the telescope is no longer a plane wave, but is a beam with a tendency to spread. The spreading angle α_{max} is given by equation (2.21), and the telescope cannot resolve objects with an angular separation less than α_{max}. Replacing w with the diameter of the lens or mirror in equation (2.21) thus yields the telescope's angular resolution. For instance, a moderate sized telescope with aperture 1 m observing red light with $\lambda \approx 6 \times 10^{-7}$ m has a maximum angular resolution of about 3×10^{-7} radians.

2.5   Two Slits

Let us now imagine a plane sine wave normally impingent on a screen with two narrow slits spaced by a distance d, as shown in figure 2.16. Since the slits are narrow relative to the wavelength of the wave impingent on them, the spreading angle of the beams is large and the diffraction pattern from each slit individually is a cylindrical wave spreading out in all directions, as illustrated in figure 2.13. The cylindrical waves from the two slits interfere, resulting in oscillations in wave intensity at the screen on the right side of figure 2.16.

Constructive interference occurs when the difference in the paths traveled by the two waves from their originating slits to the screen, $L_2 - L_1$, is an integer multiple m of the wavelength λ: $L_2 - L_1 = m\lambda$. If $L_0 \gg d$, the lines L_1 and L_2 are nearly parallel, which means that the narrow end of the dark triangle in figure 2.16 has an opening angle of θ. Thus, the path difference between the beams from the two slits is $L_2 - L_1 = d\sin\theta$. Substitution of this into the above equation shows that constructive interference occurs when

$$d\sin\theta = m\lambda, \quad m = 0, \pm 1, \pm 2, \ldots \quad \text{(two slit interference)}. \quad (2.22)$$

Destructive interference occurs when m is an integer plus $1/2$. The integer m is called the *interference order* and is the number of wavelengths by which the two paths differ.

2.6 Diffraction Gratings

Since the angular spacing $\Delta\theta$ of interference peaks in the two slit case depends on the wavelength of the incident wave, the two slit system can be used as a crude device to distinguish between the wavelengths of different components of a non-sinusoidal wave impingent on the slits. However, if more slits are added, maintaining a uniform spacing d between slits, we obtain a more sophisticated device for distinguishing beam components. This is called a *diffraction grating.*

Figures 2.17-2.19 show the intensity of the diffraction pattern as a function of position x on the display screen (see figure 2.16) for gratings with 2, 4, and 16 slits respectively, with the same slit spacing. Notice how the interference peaks remain in the same place but increase in sharpness as the number of slits increases.

The width of the peaks is actually related to the overall width of the grating, $w = nd$, where n is the number of slits. Thinking of this width as the dimension of a large single slit, the single slit equation, $\alpha_{max} = \lambda/(2w)$, tells us the angular width of the peaks.[2]

---

[2]Note that for this type of grating to work, the width of the grating has to be much less than the width of the interference peaks on the display screen. This is a severe limitation. Real diffraction grating spectrometers use a lens to focus the diffraction pattern on the screen, and are not subject to this limitation.

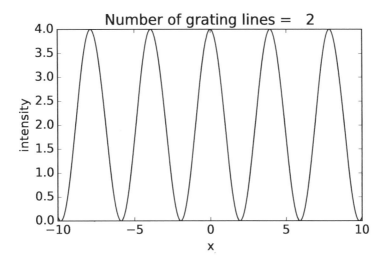

Figure 2.17: Intensity of interference pattern from a diffraction grating with 2 slits on the screen in figure 2.16. The position x on the screen is proportional to the angle θ in the small angle approximation.

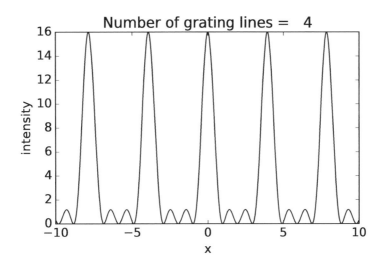

Figure 2.18: Intensity of interference pattern from a diffraction grating with 4 slits.

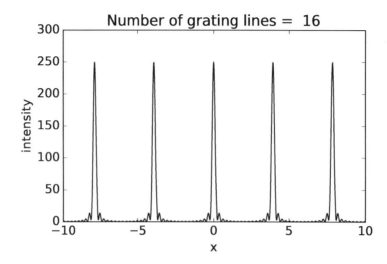

Figure 2.19: Intensity of interference pattern from a diffraction grating with 16 slits.

Whereas the angular width of the interference peaks is governed by the single slit equation, their angular positions are governed by the two slit equation. Let us assume for simplicity that $|\theta| \ll 1$ so that we can make the small angle approximation to the two slit equation, $m\lambda = d \sin \theta \approx d\theta$, and ask the following question: How different do two wavelengths differing by $\Delta\lambda$ have to be in order that the interference peaks from the two waves not overlap? In order for the peaks to be distinguishable, they should be separated in θ by an angle $\Delta\theta = m\Delta\lambda/d$, which is greater than the angular width of each peak, α_{max}:

$$\Delta\theta > \alpha_{max}. \tag{2.23}$$

Substituting in the above expressions for $\Delta\theta$ and α_{max} and solving for $\Delta\lambda$, we get $\Delta\lambda > \lambda/(2mn)$, where λ is the average of the two wavelengths and $n = w/d$ is the number of slits in the diffraction grating. Thus, the fractional difference between wavelengths which can be distinguished by a diffraction grating depends solely on the interference order m and the number of slits n in the grating:

$$\frac{\Delta\lambda}{\lambda} > \frac{1}{2mn}. \tag{2.24}$$

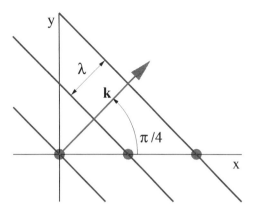

Figure 2.20: Sketch of wave moving at 45° to the x-axis.

2.7 Problems

1. Point A is at the origin. Point B is 3 m distant from A at 30° counterclockwise from the x axis. Point C is 2 m from point A at 100° counterclockwise from the x axis.

   (a) Obtain the Cartesian components of the vector $\mathbf{D}_1$ which goes from A to B and the vector $\mathbf{D}_2$ which goes from A to C.

   (b) Find the Cartesian components of the vector $\mathbf{D}_3$ which goes from B to C.

   (c) Find the direction and magnitude of $\mathbf{D}_3$.

2. For the vectors in the previous problem, find $\mathbf{D}_1 \cdot \mathbf{D}_2$ using both the cosine form of the dot product and the Cartesian form. Check to see if the two answers are the same.

3. Show graphically or otherwise that $|\mathbf{A} + \mathbf{B}| \neq |\mathbf{A}| + |\mathbf{B}|$ except when the vectors $\mathbf{A}$ and $\mathbf{B}$ are parallel.

4. A wave in the x-y plane is defined by $h = h_0 \sin(\mathbf{k} \cdot \mathbf{x})$ where $\mathbf{k} = (1, 2)$ cm^{-1}.

   (a) On a piece of graph paper draw x and y axes and then plot a line passing through the origin which is parallel to the vector $\mathbf{k}$.

(b) On the same graph plot the line defined by $\mathbf{k} \cdot \mathbf{x} = k_x x + k_y y = 0$, $\mathbf{k} \cdot \mathbf{x} = \pi$, and $\mathbf{k} \cdot \mathbf{x} = 2\pi$. Check to see if these lines are perpendicular to $\mathbf{k}$.

5. A plane wave in two dimensions in the $x - y$ plane moves in the direction $45°$ counterclockwise from the x-axis as shown in figure 2.20. Determine how fast the intersection between a wave front and the x-axis moves to the right in terms of the phase speed c of the wave. Hint: What is the distance between wave fronts along the x-axis compared to the wavelength?

6. Two deep plane ocean waves with the same frequency ω are moving approximately to the east. However, one wave is oriented a small angle β north of east and the other is oriented β south of east.

   (a) Determine the orientation of lines of constructive interference between these two waves.

   (b) Determine the spacing between lines of constructive interference.

7. An example of waves with a dispersion relation in which the frequency is a function of both wave vector magnitude and direction is shown graphically in figure 2.21.

   (a) What is the phase speed of the waves for each of the three wave vectors? Hint: You may wish to obtain the length of each wave vector graphically.

   (b) For each of the wave vectors, what is the orientation of the wave fronts?

   (c) For each of the illustrated wave vectors, sketch two other wave vectors whose average value is approximately the illustrated vector, and whose tips lie on the same frequency contour line. Determine the orientation of lines of constructive interference produced by the superimposing pairs of plane waves for which each of the vector pairs are the wave vectors.

8. Two gravity waves have the same frequency, but slightly different wavelengths.

   (a) If one wave has an orientation angle $\theta = \pi/4$ radians, what is the orientation angle of the other? (See figure 2.6.)

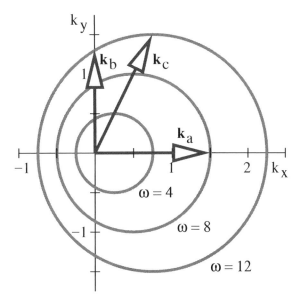

Figure 2.21: Graphical representation of the dispersion relation for shallow water waves in a river flowing in the x direction. Units of frequency are hertz, units of wavenumber are inverse meters.

    (b) Determine the orientation of lines of constructive interference between these two waves.

9. A plane wave impinges on a single slit, spreading out a half-angle α after the slit. If the whole apparatus is submerged in a liquid with index of refraction $n = 1.5$, how does the spreading angle of the light change? (Hint: Recall that the index of refraction in a transparent medium is the ratio of the speed of light in a vacuum to the speed in the medium. Furthermore, when light goes from a vacuum to a transparent medium, the light frequency doesn't change. Therefore, how does the wavelength of the light change?)

10. Determine the diameter of the telescope needed to resolve a planet 2×10^8 km from a star which is 6 light years from the earth. (Assume blue light which has a wavelength $\lambda \approx 4 \times 10^{-7}$ m $= 400$ nm. Also, don't worry about the great difference in brightness between the two for the purposes of this problem.)

11. A laser beam from a laser on the earth is bounced back to the earth by a corner reflector on the moon.

    (a) Engineers find that the returned signal is stronger if the laser beam is initially spread out by the beam expander shown in figure 2.22. Explain why this is so.

    (b) The beam has a diameter of 1 m leaving the earth. How broad is it when it reaches the moon, which is 4×10^5 km away? Assume the wavelength of the light to be 5×10^{-7} m.

    (c) How broad would the laser beam be at the moon if it weren't initially passed through the beam expander? Assume its initial diameter to be 1 cm.

12. Suppose that a plane wave impinges on two slits in a barrier at an angle, such that the phase of the wave at one slit lags the phase at the other slit by half a wavelength. How does the resulting interference pattern change from the case in which there is no lag?

13. Suppose that a thin piece of glass of index of refraction $n = 1.33$ is placed in front of one slit of a two slit diffraction setup.

    (a) How thick does the glass have to be to slow down the incoming wave so that it lags the wave going through the other slit by a phase difference of π? Take the wavelength of the light to be $\lambda = 6 \times 10^{-7}$ m.

    (b) For the above situation, describe qualitatively how the diffraction pattern changes from the case in which there is no glass in front of one of the slits. Explain your results.

14. A light source produces two wavelengths, $\lambda_1 = 400$ nm (blue) and $\lambda_2 = 600$ nm (red).

    (a) Qualitatively sketch the two slit diffraction pattern from this source. Sketch the pattern for each wavelength separately.

    (b) Qualitatively sketch the 16 slit diffraction pattern from this source, where the slit spacing is the same as in the two slit case.

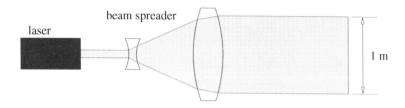

Figure 2.22: Sketch of a beam expander for a laser.

15. A light source produces two wavelengths, $\lambda_1 = 631$ nm and $\lambda_2 = 635$ nm. What is the minimum number of slits needed in a grating spectrometer to resolve the two wavelengths? (Assume that you are looking at the first order diffraction peak.) Sketch the diffraction peak from each wavelength and indicate how narrow the peaks must be to resolve them.

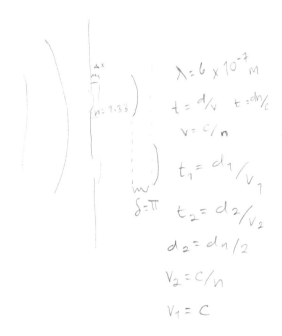

Chapter 3

Geometrical Optics

As was shown previously, when a plane wave is impingent on an aperture which has dimensions much greater than the wavelength of the wave, diffraction effects are minimal and a segment of the plane wave passes through the aperture essentially unaltered. This plane wave segment can be thought of as a wave packet, called a *beam* or *ray*, consisting of a superposition of wave vectors very close in direction and magnitude to the central wave vector of the wave packet. In most cases the ray simply moves in the direction defined by the central wave vector, i. e., normal to the orientation of the wave fronts. However, this is not true when the medium through which the light propagates is optically anisotropic, i. e., light traveling in different directions moves at different phase speeds. An example of such a medium is a calcite crystal. In the anisotropic case, the orientation of the ray can be determined once the dispersion relation for the waves in question is known, by using the techniques developed in the previous chapter.

If light moves through some apparatus in which all apertures are much greater in dimension than the wavelength of light, then we can use the above rule to follow rays of light through the apparatus. This is called the *geometrical optics* approximation.

3.1 Reflection and Refraction

Most of what we need to know about geometrical optics can be summarized in two rules, the laws of reflection and refraction. These rules may both be inferred by considering what happens when a plane wave segment impinges on

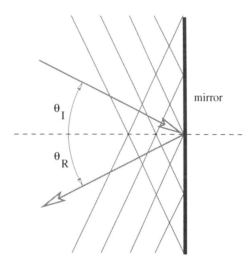

Figure 3.1: Sketch showing the reflection of a wave from a plane mirror. The law of reflection states that $\theta_I = \theta_R$.

a flat surface. If the surface is polished metal, the wave is *reflected*, whereas if the surface is an interface between two transparent media with differing indices of refraction, the wave is partially reflected and partially *refracted*. Reflection means that the wave is turned back into the half-space from which it came, while refraction means that it passes through the interface, acquiring a different direction of motion from that which it had before reaching the interface.

Figure 3.1 shows the wave vector and wave front of a wave being reflected from a plane mirror. The angles of incidence, θ_I, and reflection, θ_R, are defined to be the angles between the incoming and outgoing wave vectors respectively and the line normal to the mirror. The law of reflection states that $\theta_R = \theta_I$. This is a consequence of the need for the incoming and outgoing wave fronts to be in phase with each other all along the mirror surface. This plus the equality of the incoming and outgoing wavelengths is sufficient to insure the above result.

Refraction, as illustrated in figure 3.2, is slightly more complicated. Since $n_R > n_I$, the speed of light in the right-hand medium is less than in the left-hand medium. (Recall that the speed of light in a medium with refractive index n is $c_{medium} = c_{vac}/n$.) The frequency of the wave packet doesn't

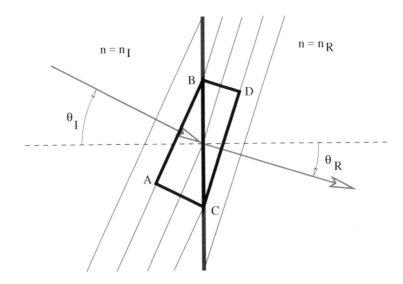

Figure 3.2: Sketch showing the refraction of a wave from an interface between two dielectric media with $n_2 > n_1$.

---

change as it passes through the interface, so the wavelength of the light on the right side is less than the wavelength on the left side.

Let us examine the triangle ABC in figure 3.2. The side AC is equal to the side BC times $\sin(\theta_I)$. However, AC is also equal to $2\lambda_I$, or twice the wavelength of the wave to the left of the interface. Similar reasoning shows that $2\lambda_R$, twice the wavelength to the right of the interface, equals BC times $\sin(\theta_R)$. Since the interval BC is common to triangles ABC and DBC, we easily see that

$$\frac{\lambda_I}{\lambda_R} = \frac{\sin(\theta_I)}{\sin(\theta_R)}. \tag{3.1}$$

Since $\lambda_I = c_I T = c_{vac} T / n_I$ and $\lambda_R = c_R T = c_{vac} T / n_R$ where c_I and c_R are the wave speeds to the left and right of the interface, c_{vac} is the speed of light in a vacuum, and T is the (common) period, we can easily recast the above equation in the form

$$n_I \sin(\theta_I) = n_R \sin(\theta_R). \tag{3.2}$$

This is called *Snell's law*, and it governs how a ray of light bends as it passes through a discontinuity in the index of refraction. The angle θ_I is called the incident angle and θ_R is called the refracted angle. Notice that these angles are measured from the normal to the surface, not the tangent.

3.2 Total Internal Reflection

When light passes from a medium of lesser index of refraction to one with greater index of refraction, Snell's law indicates that the ray bends *toward* the normal to the interface. The reverse occurs when the passage is in the other direction. In this latter circumstance a special situation arises when Snell's law predicts a value for the sine of the refracted angle greater than one. This is physically untenable. What actually happens is that the incident wave is *reflected* from the interface. This phenomenon is called *total internal reflection*. The minimum incident angle for which total internal reflection occurs is obtained by substituting $\theta_R = \pi/2$ into equation (3.2), resulting in

$$\sin(\theta_I) = n_R/n_I \quad \text{(total internal reflection)}. \tag{3.3}$$

3.3 Anisotropic Media

Notice that Snell's law makes the implicit assumption that rays of light move in the direction of the light's wave vector, i. e., normal to the wave fronts. As the analysis in the previous chapter makes clear, this is valid only when the optical medium is isotropic, i. e., the wave frequency depends only on the magnitude of the wave vector, not on its direction.

Certain kinds of crystals, such as those made of calcite, are not isotropic — the speed of light in such crystals, and hence the wave frequency, depends on the orientation of the wave vector. As an example, the angular frequency in an anisotropic medium might take the form

$$\omega = \left[\frac{c_1^2(k_x + k_y)^2}{2} + \frac{c_2^2(k_x - k_y)^2}{2} \right]^{1/2}, \tag{3.4}$$

where c_1 is the speed of light for waves in which $k_y = k_x$, and c_2 is its speed when $k_y = -k_x$.

Figure 3.3 shows an example in which a ray hits a calcite crystal oriented so that constant frequency contours are as specified in equation (3.4). The wave vector is oriented normal to the surface of the crystal, so that wave

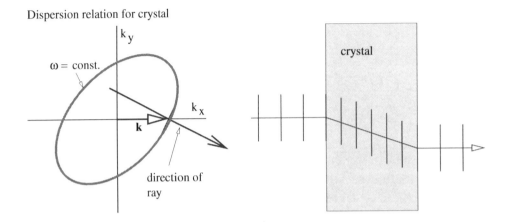

Figure 3.3: The right panel shows the fate of a light ray normally incident on the face of a properly cut calcite crystal. The anisotropic dispersion relation which gives rise to this behavior is shown in the left panel.

fronts are parallel to this surface. Upon entering the crystal, the wave front orientation must stay the same to preserve phase continuity at the surface. However, due to the anisotropy of the dispersion relation for light in the crystal, the ray direction changes as shown in the right panel. This behavior is clearly inconsistent with the usual version of Snell's law!

It is possible to extend Snell's law to the anisotropic case. However, we will not present this here. The following discussions of optical instruments will always assume that isotropic optical media are used.

3.4   Thin Lens Equation and Optical Instruments

Given the laws of reflection and refraction, one can see in principle how the passage of light through an optical instrument could be traced. For each of a number of initial rays, the change in the direction of the ray at each mirror surface or refractive index interface can be calculated. Between these points, the ray traces out a straight line.

Though simple in conception, this procedure can be quite complex in practice. However, the procedure simplifies if a number of approximations,

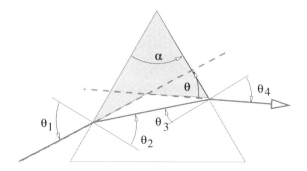

Figure 3.4: Bending of a ray of light as it passes through a prism.

collectively called the *thin lens approximation*, are valid. We begin with the calculation of the bending of a ray of light as it passes through a prism, as illustrated in figure 3.4.

The pieces of information needed to find θ, the angle through which the ray is deflected, are as follows: the geometry of the triangle defined by the entry and exit points of the ray and the upper vertex of the prism leads to

$$\alpha + (\pi/2 - \theta_2) + (\pi/2 - \theta_3) = \pi, \qquad (3.5)$$

which simplifies to

$$\alpha = \theta_2 + \theta_3. \qquad (3.6)$$

Snell's law at the entrance and exit points of the ray tell us that

$$n = \frac{\sin(\theta_1)}{\sin(\theta_2)} \qquad n = \frac{\sin(\theta_4)}{\sin(\theta_3)}, \qquad (3.7)$$

where n is the index of refraction of the prism. (The index of refraction of the surroundings is assumed to be unity.) One can also infer that

$$\theta = \theta_1 + \theta_4 - \alpha. \qquad (3.8)$$

This comes from the fact that the the sum of the internal angles of the shaded quadrangle in figure 3.4 is

$$(\pi/2 - \theta_1) + \alpha + (\pi/2 - \theta_4) + (\pi + \theta) = 2\pi. \qquad (3.9)$$

Combining equations (3.6), (3.7), and (3.8) allows the ray deflection θ to be determined in terms of θ_1 and α, but the resulting expression is very

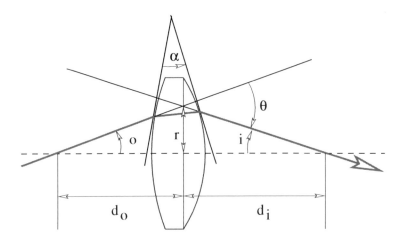

Figure 3.5: Light ray undergoing deflection through an angle θ by a lens. The angle α is the angle between the tangents to the entry and exit points of the ray on the lens.

---

messy. However, great simplification occurs if the following conditions are met:

- The angle $\alpha \ll 1$.

- The angles θ_1, θ_2, θ_3, $\theta_4 \ll 1$.

With these approximations it is easy to show that

$$\theta = \alpha(n-1) \quad \text{(small angles)}. \tag{3.10}$$

Generally speaking, lenses and mirrors in optical instruments have curved rather than flat surfaces. However, we can still use the laws for reflection and refraction by plane surfaces as long as the segment of the surface on which the wave packet impinges is not curved very much on the scale of the wave packet dimensions. This condition is easy to satisfy with light impinging on ordinary optical instruments. In this case, the deflection of a ray of light is given by equation (3.10) if α is defined as the intersection of the tangent lines to the entry and exit points of the ray, as illustrated in figure 3.5.

A *positive lens* is thicker in the center than at the edges. The angle α between the tangent lines to the two surfaces of the lens at a distance r

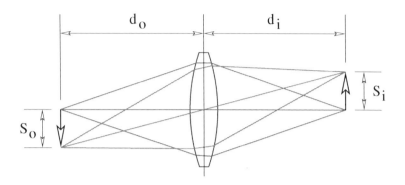

Figure 3.6: A positive lens producing an image on the right of the arrow on the left.

from the central axis takes the form $\alpha = Cr$, where C is a constant. The deflection angle of a beam hitting the lens a distance r from the center is therefore $\theta = Cr(n-1)$, as indicated in figure 3.5. The angles o and i sum to the deflection angle: $o + i = \theta = Cr(n-1)$. However, to the extent that the small angle approximation holds, $o = r/d_o$ and $i = r/d_i$ where d_o is the distance to the object and d_i is the distance to the image of the object. Putting these equations together and cancelling the r results in the *thin lens equation*:

$$\frac{1}{d_o} + \frac{1}{d_i} = C(n-1) \equiv \frac{1}{f}. \tag{3.11}$$

The quantity f is called the *focal length* of the lens. Notice that $f = d_i$ if the object is very far from the lens, i. e., if d_o is extremely large.

Figure 3.6 shows how a positive lens makes an image. The image is produced by all of the light from each point on the object falling on a corresponding point in the image. If the arrow on the left is an illuminated object, an *image* of the arrow will appear at right if the light coming from the lens is allowed to fall on a piece of paper or a ground glass screen. The size of the object S_o and the size of the image S_i are related by simple geometry to the distances of the object and the image from the lens:

$$\frac{S_i}{S_o} = \frac{d_i}{d_o}. \tag{3.12}$$

Notice that a positive lens inverts the image.

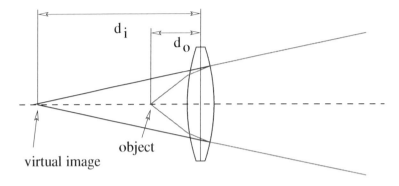

Figure 3.7: Production of a virtual image by a positive lens.

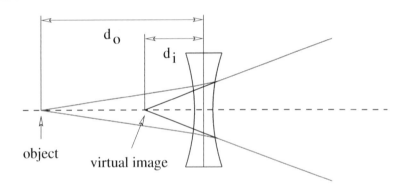

Figure 3.8: Production of a virtual image by a negative lens.

An image will be produced to the right of the lens only if $d_o > f$. If $d_o < f$, the lens is unable to converge the rays from the image to a point, as is seen in figure 3.7. However, in this case the backward extension of the rays converge at a point called a *virtual image*, which in the case of a positive lens is always farther away from the lens than the object. The image is called virtual because it does not appear on a ground glass screen placed at this point. Unlike the real image seen in figure 3.6, the virtual image is not inverted. The thin lens equation still applies if the distance from the lens to the image is taken to be negative.

A *negative lens* is thinner in the center than at the edges and produces only virtual images. As seen in figure 3.8, the virtual image produced by a

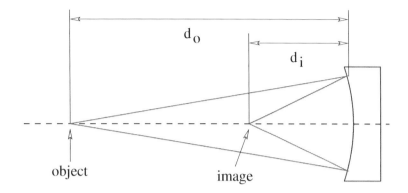

Figure 3.9: Production of a real image by a concave mirror.

negative lens is closer to the lens than is the object. Again, the thin lens equation is still valid, but both the distance from the image to the lens and the focal length must be taken as negative. Only the distance to the object remains positive.

Curved mirrors also produce images in a manner similar to a lens, as shown in figure 3.9. A concave mirror, as seen in this figure, works in analogy to a positive lens, producing a real or a virtual image depending on whether the object is farther from or closer to the mirror than the mirror's focal length. A convex mirror acts like a negative lens, always producing a virtual image. The thin lens equation works in both cases as long as the angles are small.

3.5   Fermat's Principle

An alternate approach to geometrical optics can be developed from Fermat's principle. This principle states (in its simplest form) that light waves of a given frequency traverse the path between two points which takes the least time. The most obvious example of this is the passage of light through a homogeneous medium in which the speed of light doesn't change with position. In this case the shortest time corresponds to the shortest distance between the points, which, as we all know, is a straight line. Thus, Fermat's principle is consistent with light traveling in a straight line in a homogeneous medium.

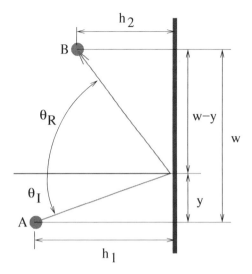

Figure 3.10: Definition sketch for deriving the law of reflection from Fermat's principle. θ_I is the angle of incidence and θ_R the angle of reflection as in figure 3.1.

Fermat's principle can also be used to derive the laws of reflection and refraction. For instance, figure 3.10 shows a candidate ray for reflection in which the angles of incidence and reflection are not equal. The time required for the light to go from point A to point B is

$$t = ([h_1^2 + y^2]^{1/2} + [h_2^2 + (w - y)^2]^{1/2})/c \qquad (3.13)$$

where c is the speed of light. We find the minimum time by differentiating t with respect to y and setting the result to zero, with the result that

$$\frac{y}{[h_1^2 + y^2]^{1/2}} = \frac{w - y}{[h_2^2 + (w - y)^2]^{1/2}}. \qquad (3.14)$$

However, we note that the left side of this equation is simply $\sin \theta_I$, while the right side is $\sin \theta_R$, so that the minimum time condition reduces to $\sin \theta_I = \sin \theta_R$ or $\theta_I = \theta_R$, which is the law of reflection.

A similar analysis may be done to derive Snell's law of refraction. The speed of light in a medium with refractive index n is c/n, where c is its speed in a vacuum. Thus, the time required for light to go some distance in such a

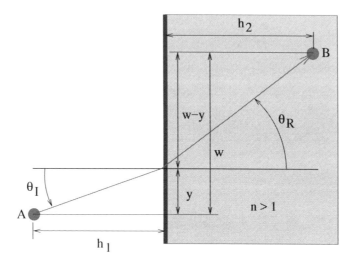

Figure 3.11: Definition sketch for deriving Snell's law of refraction from Fermat's principle. The shaded area has index of refraction $n > 1$.

medium is n times the time light takes to go the same distance in a vacuum. Referring to figure 3.11, the time required for light to go from A to B becomes

$$t = ([h_1^2 + y^2]^{1/2} + n[h_2^2 + (w - y)^2]^{1/2})/c. \qquad (3.15)$$

This results in the condition

$$\sin \theta_I = n \sin \theta_R \qquad (3.16)$$

where θ_R is now the refracted angle. We recognize this result as Snell's law.

Notice that the reflection case illustrates a point about Fermat's principle: The minimum time may actually be a *local* rather than a global minimum — after all, in figure 3.10, the global minimum distance from A to B is still just a straight line between the two points! In fact, light starting from point A will reach point B by *both* routes — the direct route and the reflected route.

It turns out that trajectories allowed by Fermat's principle don't strictly have to be minimum time trajectories. They can also be *maximum* time trajectories, as illustrated in figure 3.12. In this case light emitted at point O can be reflected back to point O from four points on the mirror, A, B, C, and D. The trajectories O-A-O and O-C-O are minimum time trajectories while O-B-O and O-D-O are maximum time trajectories.

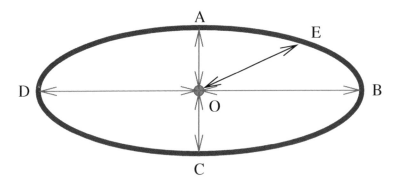

Figure 3.12: Ellipsoidal mirror showing minimum and maximum time rays from the center of the ellipsoid to the mirror surface and back again.

Fermat's principle seems rather mysterious. However, the American physicist Richard Feynman made sense out of it by invoking an even more fundamental principle, as we now see.

If a light ray originates at point O in figure 3.12, reflects off of the ellipsoidal mirror surface at point A, and returns to point O, the elapsed time isn't much different from that experienced by a ray which reflects off the mirror a slight distance from point A and returns to O. This is because at point A the beam from point O is perpendicular to the tangent to the surface of the mirror at point A. In contrast, the time experienced by a ray going from point O to point E and back would differ by a much greater amount than the time experienced by a ray reflecting off the mirror a slight distance from point E. This is because the tangent to the mirror surface at point E is not perpendicular to the beam from point O.

Technically, the change in the round trip time varies linearly with the deviation in the reflection point from point E, but quadratically with the deviation from point A. If this deviation is small in the first place, then the change in the round trip time will be much smaller for the quadratic case than for the linear case.

It seems odd that we would speak of a beam reflecting back to point O if it hit the mirror at any point except A, B, C, or D, due to the requirements of the law of reflection. However, recall that the law of reflection itself depends on Fermat's principle, so we cannot assume the validity of that law in this investigation.

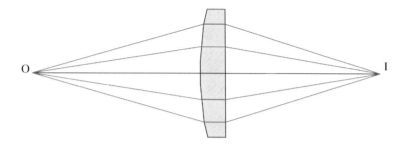

Figure 3.13: Ray trajectories from a point O being focused to another point I by a lens.

Feynman postulated that light rays explore *all* possible paths from one point to another, but that the only paths realized in nature are those for which light taking closely neighboring paths experiences nearly the same elapsed time (or more generally, traverses nearly the same number of wavelengths) as the original path. If this is true, then neighboring rays interfere constructively with each other, resulting in a much brighter beam than would occur in the absence of this constructive interference. Thus, the round-trip paths O-A-O, O-B-O, O-C-O, and O-D-O in figure 3.12 actually occur, but not O-E-O. Feynman explains Fermat's principle by invoking constructive and destructive interference!

Figure 3.13 illustrates a rather peculiar situation. Notice that *all* the rays from point O which intercept the lens end up at point I. This would seem to contradict Fermat's principle, in that only the minimum (or maximum) time trajectories should occur. However, a calculation shows that all the illustrated trajectories in this particular case take the *same* time. Thus, the light cannot choose one trajectory over another using Fermat's principle and all of the trajectories are equally favored. Note that this inference applies not to just any set of trajectories, but only those going from an object point to the corresponding image point.

3.6 Problems

1. The index of refraction varies as shown in figure 3.14:

    (a) Given θ_1, use Snell's law to find θ_2.

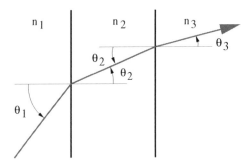

Figure 3.14: Refraction through multiple parallel layers with different refractive indices.

Figure 3.15: Refraction through a 45°-45°-90° prism.

(b) Given θ_2, use Snell's law to find θ_3.

(c) From the above results, find θ_3, given θ_1. Do n_2 or θ_2 matter?

2. A 45°-45°-90° prism is used to totally reflect light through 90° as shown in figure 3.15. What is the minimum index of refraction of the prism needed for this to work?

3. Show graphically which way the wave vector must point inside the calcite crystal of figure 3.3 for a light ray to be horizontally oriented. Sketch the orientation of the wave fronts in this case.

4. The human eye is a lens which focuses images on a screen called the retina. Suppose that the normal focal length of this lens is 4 cm and that this focuses images from far away objects on the retina. Let us assume that the eye is able to focus on nearby objects by changing the

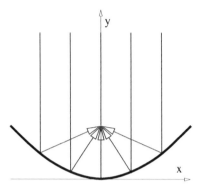

Figure 3.16: Focusing of parallel rays by a parabolic mirror.

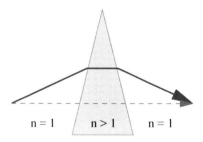

Figure 3.17: Refraction through a wedge-shaped prism.

Figure 3.18: An amoeba imaged by a lens.

shape of the lens, and thus its focal length. (The lens-retina distance remains the same.) If an object is 20 cm from the eye, what must the altered focal length of the eye be in order for the image of this object to be in focus on the retina?

5. An amoeba 0.01 cm in diameter has its image projected on a screen as shown in figure 3.18 by a positive lens of diameter 0.1 cm.

   (a) How big is the image of the amoeba?

   (b) What is the focal length of the lens?

   (c) What is the minimum distance between features on the image of the amoeba which can be resolved? Assume that the wavelength of light used is 5×10^{-7} m. (Hint: What is the spreading angle of a beam of light passing through an opening the size of the lens?)

6. The great refractor telescope of Yerkes Observatory in Wisconsin (see figure 3.19) has primary lens $D = 1.02$ m in diameter with a focal length of $L = 19.4$ m. Use the small angle approximation in all calculations and assume that the light has wavelength 5×10^{-7} m.

   (a) Jupiter has a diameter of 1.5×10^5 km and an average distance from the earth of 8×10^8 km. How big is the image of Jupiter (in cm) at the focal plane of the primary lens?

   (b) Given perfect atmospheric "seeing" conditions, how far apart must two features be on Jupiter (in km) for the Yerkes telescope to be able to resolve them?

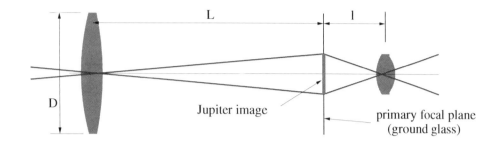

Figure 3.19: The great Yerkes refractor telescope observing Jupiter.

(c) What should the focal length l of the secondary lens or eyepiece be
for Jupiter to subtend the same angle as the moon subtends to the
naked eye? The moon's diameter is 3.5×10^3 km and its distance
from the earth is 3.8×10^5 km. Hint: Imagine that a translucent
sheet of ground glass is placed at the focal plane so that the image
is seen projected on this ground glass, which scatters light over a
broad range of angles. The eyepiece can then be thought of as a
magnifying glass with which you can examine the image on the
ground glass. Using this artiface, you need consider only light rays
that pass through the center of each lens.

7. Show that a concave mirror that focuses incoming rays parallel to the
optical axis of the mirror to a point on the optical axis, as illustrated in
figure 3.16, is parabolic in shape. Hint: Since rays following different
paths all move from the distant source to the focal point of the mirror,
Fermat's principle implies that all of these rays take the same time to
do so (why is this?), and therefore all traverse the same distance.

8. Use *Fermat's principle* to explain *qualitatively* why a ray of light follows
the solid rather than the dashed line through the wedge of glass shown
in figure 3.17.

9. Test your knowledge of Fermat's principle by using equation (3.15) to
derive Snell's law.

Chapter 4

Special Relativity

Albert Einstein invented the special and general theories of relativity early in the 20th century, though many other people contributed to the intellectual climate which made these discoveries possible. The special theory of relativity arose out of a conflict between the ideas of mechanics as developed by Galileo and Newton, and the theory of electromagnetism. For this reason relativity is often discussed in textbooks after electromagnetism is developed. However, special relativity is actually a valid extension to the Galilean world view which is needed when objects move at very high speeds, and it is only coincidentally related to electromagnetism. For this reason we discuss relativity before electromagnetism.

The only fact from electromagnetism that we need is introduced now: There is a maximum speed at which objects can travel. This is coincidentally equal to the speed of light in a vacuum, $c = 3 \times 10^8$ m s^{-1}. Furthermore, a measurement of the speed of a particular light beam yields the same answer regardless of the speed of the light source or the speed at which the measuring instrument is moving.

This rather bizarre experimental result is in contrast to what occurs in Galilean relativity. If two cars pass a pedestrian standing on a curb, one at 20 m s^{-1} and the other at 50 m s^{-1}, the faster car appears to be moving at 30 m s^{-1} relative to the slower car. However, if a light beam moving at 3×10^8 m s^{-1} passes an interstellar spaceship moving at 2×10^8 m s^{-1}, then the light beam appears to occupants of the spaceship to be moving at 3×10^8 m s^{-1}, not 1×10^8 m s^{-1}. Furthermore, if the spaceship beams a light signal forward to its (stationary) destination planet, then the resulting beam appears to be moving at 3×10^8 m s^{-1} to instruments at the destination, not

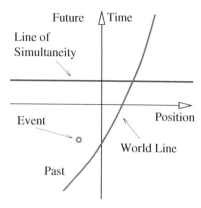

Figure 4.1: Spacetime diagram showing an *event*, a *world line*, and a *line of simultaneity*.

5×10^8 m s^{-1}.

The fact that we are talking about light beams is only for convenience. Any other means of sending a signal at the maximum allowed speed would result in the same behavior. We therefore cannot seek the answer to this apparent paradox in the special properties of light. Instead we have to look to the basic nature of space and time.

4.1   Galilean Spacetime Thinking

In order to gain an understanding of both Galilean and Einsteinian relativity it is important to begin thinking of space and time as being different dimensions of a four-dimensional space called spacetime. Actually, since we can't visualize four dimensions very well, it is easiest to start with only one space dimension and the time dimension. Figure 4.1 shows a graph with time plotted on the vertical axis and the one space dimension plotted on the horizontal axis. An *event* is something that occurs at a particular time and a particular point in space. ("Julius X. wrecks his car in Lemitar, NM on 21 June at 6:17 PM.") A *world line* is a plot of the position of some object as a function of time on a spacetime diagram, although it is conventional to put time on the vertical axis. Thus, a world line is really a line in spacetime, while an event is a point in spacetime. A horizontal line parallel to the position axis is a *line of simultaneity* in Galilean relativity — i. e., all events on this line occur simultaneously.

In a spacetime diagram the slope of a world line has a special meaning. Notice that a vertical world line means that the object it represents does not move — the velocity is zero. If the object moves to the right, then the world line tilts to the right, and the faster it moves, the more the world line tilts. Quantitatively, we say that

$$velocity = \frac{1}{slope\ of\ world\ line} \qquad (4.1)$$

in Galilean relativity. Notice that this works for negative slopes and velocities as well as positive ones. If the object changes its velocity with time, then the world line is curved, and the instantaneous velocity at any time is the inverse of the slope of the tangent to the world line at that time.

The hardest thing to realize about spacetime diagrams is that they represent the past, present, and future all in one diagram. Thus, spacetime diagrams don't change with time — the evolution of physical systems is represented by looking at successive horizontal slices in the diagram at successive times. *Spacetime diagrams represent evolution, but they don't evolve themselves.*

The principle of relativity states that the laws of physics are the same in all inertial reference frames. An inertial reference frame is one that is not accelerated. Reference frames attached to a car at rest and to a car moving steadily down the freeway at 30 m s^{-1} are both inertial. A reference frame attached to a car accelerating away from a stop light is not inertial.

The principle of relativity is an educated guess or hypothesis based on extensive experience. If the principle of relativity weren't true, we would have to do all our calculations in some preferred reference frame. This would be very annoying. However, the more fundamental problem is that we have no idea what the velocity of this preferred frame might be. Does it move with the earth? That would be very earth-centric. How about the velocity of the center of our galaxy or the mean velocity of all the galaxies? Rather than face the issue of a preferred reference frame, physicists have chosen to stick with the principle of relativity.

If an object is moving to the left at velocity v relative to a particular reference frame, it appears to be moving at a velocity $v' = v - U$ relative to another reference frame which itself is moving at velocity U. This is the Galilean velocity transformation law, and it is based on everyday experience.

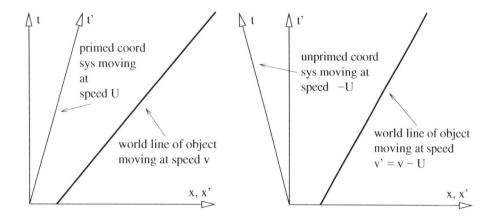

Figure 4.2: The left panel shows the world line in the unprimed reference frame, while the right panel shows it in the primed frame, which moves to the right at speed U relative to the unprimed frame. (The "prime" is just a label that allows us to distinguish the axes corresponding to the two reference frames.)

If you are traveling 30 m s^{-1} down the freeway and another car passes you doing 40 m s^{-1}, then the other car moves past you at 10 m s^{-1} relative to your car.

Figure 4.2 shows how the world line of an object is represented differently in the unprimed (x, t) and primed (x', t') reference frames. The difference between the velocity of the object and the velocity of the primed frame (i. e., the difference in the inverses of the slopes of the corresponding world lines) is the same in both reference frames in this Galilean case. This illustrates the difference between a physical law independent of reference frame (the difference between velocities in Galilean relativity) and the different motion of the object in the two different reference frames.

4.2   Spacetime Thinking in Special Relativity

In special relativity we find that space and time "mix" in a way that they don't in Galilean relativity. This suggests that space and time are different aspects of the same "thing", which we call *spacetime*.

If time and position are simply different dimensions of the same abstract

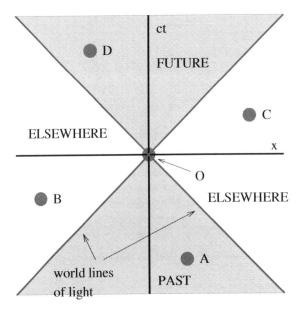

Figure 4.3: Scaled spacetime diagram showing world lines of light passing left and right through the origin.

---

space, then they should have the same units. The easiest way to arrange this is to multiply time by the maximum speed, c, resulting in the kind of spacetime diagram shown in figure 4.3. Notice that world lines of light have slope ± 1 when the time axis is scaled this way. Furthermore, the relationship between speed and the slope of a world line must be revised to read

$$v = \frac{c}{slope} \quad \text{(world line)}. \tag{4.2}$$

Notice that it is physically possible for an object to have a world line which connects event O at the origin and the events A and D in figure 4.3, since the slope of the resulting world line would exceed unity, and thus represent a velocity less than the speed of light. Events which can be connected by a world line are called *timelike* relative to each other. On the other hand, event O cannot be connected to events B and C by a world line, since this would imply a velocity greater than the speed of light. Events which cannot be connected by a world line are called *spacelike* relative to each other. Notice the terminology in figure 4.3: Event A is in the *past* of event O, while event

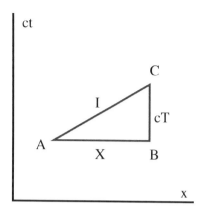

Figure 4.4: Triangle for Pythagorean theorem in spacetime.

D is in the *future*. Events B and C are *elsewhere* relative to event O.

4.3   Postulates of Special Relativity

As we learned previously, the *principle of relativity* states that the laws of physics are the same in all inertial reference frames. The principle of relativity applies to Einsteinian relativity just as it applies to Galilean relativity.

Notice that the constancy of the speed of light in all reference frames is consistent with the principle of relativity. However, as noted above, it is inconsistent with our notions as to how velocities add, or alternatively, how we think the world should look from reference frames moving at different speeds. We have called the classical way of understanding the view from different reference frames Galilean relativity. The new way that reconciles the behavior of objects moving at very high speeds is called *Einsteinian relativity*. Einstein's great contribution was to discover the laws that tell us how the world looks from reference frames moving at high speeds relative to each other. These laws constitute a *geometry of spacetime*, and from them all of special relativity can be derived.

All of the observed facts about spacetime can be derived from two postulates:

- Whether two events are simultaneous depends on the reference frame from which they are viewed.

- Spacetime obeys a modified Pythagorean theorem, which gives the distance, I, in spacetime or *spacetime interval* as

$$I^2 = X^2 - c^2 T^2, \tag{4.3}$$

where X, T, and I are defined in figure 4.4.

Let us discuss these postulates in turn.

4.3.1 Simultaneity

The classical way of thinking about *simultaneity* is so ingrained in our everyday habits that we have a great deal of difficulty adjusting to what special relativity has to say about this subject. Indeed, understanding how relativity changes this concept is the single most difficult part of the theory — once you understand this, you are well on your way to mastering relativity!

Before tackling simultaneity, let us first think about *collocation*. Two events (such as A and E in figure 4.5) are collocated if they have the same x value. However, collocation is a concept that depends on the reference frame. For instance, George is driving from Boston to Washington, with the line passing through events A and D being his world line. Just as he passes New York he sneezes (event A in figure 4.5). As he drives by Baltimore, he sneezes again (event D). In the reference frame of the earth, these two sneezes are not collocated, since they are separated by many kilometers. However, in the reference frame of George's car, they occur in the same place — assuming that George hasn't left the driver's seat!

Notice that any two events separated by a timelike interval are collocated in *some* reference frame. The speed of the reference frame is given by equation (4.2), where the slope is simply the slope of the world line connecting the two events.

In Galilean relativity, if two events are simultaneous, we consider them to be simultaneous in all reference frames. For instance, if two clocks, one in New York and one in Los Angeles, strike the hour at the same time in the earth reference frame, then in Galilean relativity these events also appear to be simultaneous to instruments in the space shuttle as it flies over the United States. However, if the space shuttle is moving from west to east, i. e., from Los Angeles toward New York, careful measurements will show that the clock in New York strikes the hour *before* the clock in Los Angeles! Thus, the Galilean point of view is not accurate.

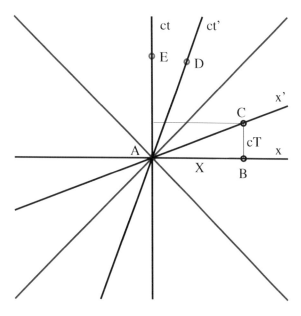

Figure 4.5: Sketch of coordinate axes for a moving reference frame, x', ct'. The meanings of the events A-E are discussed in the text. The lines tilted at $\pm 45°$ are the world lines of light passing through the origin.

Just as collocation depends on one's reference frame, this result shows that simultaneity also depends on the reference frame. Figure 4.5 shows how this works. In figure 4.5 events A and B are simultaneous in the rest or unprimed reference frame. However, in the primed reference frame, events A and C are simultaneous, and event B occurs at an earlier time. If A and B correspond to the clocks striking in Los Angeles and New York respectively, then it is clear that B must occur at an earlier time in the primed frame if indeed A and C are simultaneous in that frame.

The tilted line passing through events A and C in figure 4.5 is called the *line of simultaneity* for the primed reference frame. Its slope is related to the speed, U, of the reference frame by

$$slope = U/c \quad \text{(line of simultaneity)}. \tag{4.4}$$

Notice that this is the inverse of the slope of the world line attached to the primed reference frame. There is thus a symmetry between the world line and the line of simultaneity of a moving reference frame — as the reference

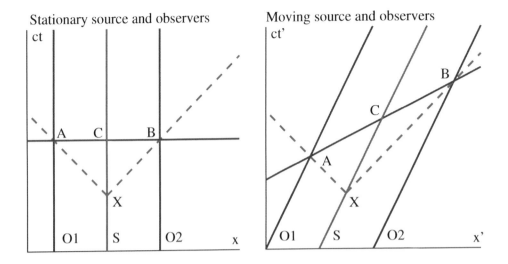

Figure 4.6: World lines of two observers (O1, O2) and a pulsed light source (S) equidistant between them. In the left frame the observers and the source are all stationary. In the right frame they are all moving to the right at half the speed of light. The dashed lines show pulses of light emitted simultaneously to the left and the right.

---

frame moves faster to the right, these two lines close like the blades of a pair of scissors on the 45° line.

In Galilean relativity it is fairly obvious what we mean by two events being simultaneous — it all boils down to coordinating portable clocks which are sitting next to each other, and then moving them to the desired locations. Two events separated in space are simultaneous if they occur at the same time on clocks located near each event, assuming that the clocks have been coordinated in the above manner.

In Einsteinian relativity this doesn't work, because the very act of moving the clocks changes the rate at which the clocks run. Thus, it is more difficult to determine whether two distant events are simultaneous.

An alternate way of experimentally determining simultaneity is shown in figure 4.6. Since we know from observation that light travels at the same speed in all reference frames, the pulses of light emitted by the light sources in figure 4.6 will reach the two equidistant observers simultaneously in both cases. The line passing through these two events, A and B, defines a line of simultaneity for both stationary and moving observers. For the stationary observers this line is horizontal, as in Galilean relativity. For the moving observers the light has to travel farther in the rest frame to reach the observer receding from the light source, and it therefore takes longer in this frame. Thus, event B in the right panel of figure 4.6 occurs later than event A in the stationary reference frame and the line of simultaneity is tilted. We see that the postulate that light moves at the same speed in all reference frames leads inevitably to the dependence of simultaneity on reference frame.

4.3.2 Spacetime Pythagorean Theorem

The Pythagorean theorem of spacetime differs from the usual Pythagorean theorem in two ways. First, the vertical side of the triangle is multiplied by c. This is a trivial scale factor that gives time the same units as space. Second, the right side of equation (4.3) has a minus sign rather than a plus sign. This highlights a fundamental difference between spacetime and the ordinary xyz space in which we live. Spacetime is said to have a *non-Euclidean* (but not curved) geometry — in other words, the normal rules of geometry that we learn in high school don't always work for spacetime!

The main consequence of the minus sign in equation (4.3) is that I^2 can be negative and therefore I can be imaginary. Furthermore, in the special case where $X = \pm cT$, we actually have $I = 0$ even though X, $T \neq 0$ — i. e., the "distance" between two well-separated events can be zero. Clearly, spacetime has some weird properties!

The quantity I is usually called an *interval* in spacetime. Generally speaking, if I^2 is positive, the interval is called *spacelike*, while for a negative I^2, the interval is called *timelike*.

A concept related to the spacetime interval is the *proper time τ*. The proper time between the two events A and C in figure 4.4 is defined by the equation

$$\tau^2 = T^2 - X^2/c^2. \tag{4.5}$$

Notice that I and τ are related by

$$\tau^2 = -I^2/c^2, \tag{4.6}$$

so the spacetime interval and the proper time are not independent concepts. However, I has the dimensions of length and is real when the events defining the interval are spacelike relative to each other, whereas τ has the dimensions of time and is real when the events are timelike relative to each other. Both equation (4.3) and equation (4.5) express the spacetime Pythagorean theorem.

If two events defining the end points of an interval have the same t value, then the interval is the ordinary space distance between the two events. On the other hand, if they have the same x value, then the proper time is just the time interval between the events. If the interval between two events is spacelike, but the events are not simultaneous in the initial reference frame, they can always be made simultaneous by choosing a reference frame in which the events lie on the same line of simultaneity. Thus, the meaning of the interval in that case is just the distance between the events in the new reference frame. Similarly, for events separated by a timelike interval, the proper time is just the time between two events in a reference frame in which the two events are collocated.

4.4 Time Dilation

Stationary and moving clocks run at different rates in relativity. This is illustrated in figure 4.7. The triangle ABC in the left panel of figure 4.7 can be used to illustrate this point. Suppose that the line passing through the events A and C in this figure is the world line of a stationary observer. At zero time another observer moving with velocity V passes the stationary observer. The moving observer's world line passes through events A and B.

We assume that events B and C are simultaneous in the rest frame, so ABC is a right triangle. Application of the spacetime Pythagorean theorem thus yields

$$c^2 T'^2 = c^2 T^2 - X^2. \tag{4.7}$$

Since the second observer is moving at velocity V, the slope of his world line is

$$\frac{c}{V} = \frac{cT}{X}, \tag{4.8}$$

where the right side of the above equation is the slope calculated as the rise of the world line cT over the run X between events A and B. Eliminating X between the above two equations results in a relationship between T and T':

$$T' = T(1 - V^2/c^2)^{1/2} \equiv T/\gamma, \tag{4.9}$$

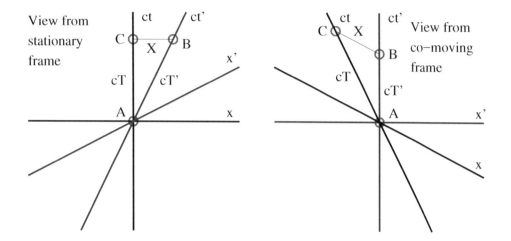

Figure 4.7: Two views of the relationship between three events, A, B, and C. The left panel shows the view from the unprimed reference frame, in which A and C are collocated, while the right panel shows the view from the primed frame, in which A and B are collocated.

where

$$\gamma = \frac{1}{(1 - V^2/c^2)^{1/2}}. \tag{4.10}$$

The quantity γ occurs so often in relativistic calculations that we give it this special symbol. Note by its definition that $\gamma \geq 1$.

Equation (4.9) tells us that the time elapsed for the moving observer is less than that for the stationary observer, which means that the clock of the moving observer runs more slowly. This is called the *time dilation* effect.

Let us view this situation from the reference frame of the moving observer. In this frame the moving observer becomes stationary and the stationary observer moves in the opposite direction, as illustrated in the right panel of figure 4.7. By symmetric arguments, one infers that the clock of the initially stationary observer who is now moving to the left runs more slowly in this reference frame than the clock of the initially moving observer. One might conclude that this contradicts the previous results. However, examination of the right panel of figure 4.7 shows that this is not so. The interval cT is still greater than the interval cT', because such intervals are relativistically invariant quantities. However, events B and C are no longer simultaneous,

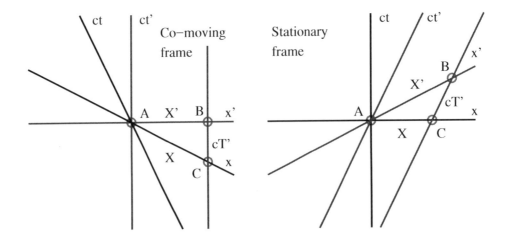

Figure 4.8: Definition sketch for understanding the Lorentz contraction. The parallel lines represent the world lines of the front and the rear of a moving object. The left panel shows a reference frame moving with the object, while the right panel shows a stationary reference frame.

---

so one cannot use these results to infer anything about the rate at which the two clocks run in this frame. Thus, the relative nature of the concept of simultaneity saves us from an incipient paradox, and we see that the relative rates at which clocks run depends on the reference frame in which these rates are observed.

4.5   Lorentz Contraction

A similar argument can be made to show how the postulates of relativity result in the *Lorentz contraction*. Figure 4.8 compares the length X' of a moving object measured in its own reference frame (left panel) with its length X as measured in a stationary reference frame (right panel). The length of a moving object is measured by *simultaneously* measuring the positions of the front and the rear of the object and subtracting these two numbers. Events A and C correspond to these position measurements for the stationary reference frame since they are respectively on the rear and front world lines of the object. Thus, the interval AC, which is equal to X, is the length of the object as measured in the stationary frame.

In the left panel, X is the hypotenuse of a right triangle. Therefore, by the Pythagorean theorem of spacetime, we have

$$X = I = (X'^2 - c^2 T'^2)^{1/2}. \qquad (4.11)$$

Now, the line passing through A and C in the left panel is the line of simultaneity of the stationary reference frame. The slope of this line is $-V/c$, where V is the speed of the object relative to the stationary reference frame. Geometrically in figure 4.8, the slope of this line is $-cT'/X'$, so we find by equating these two expressions for the slope that

$$T' = V X'/c^2. \qquad (4.12)$$

Finally, eliminating T' between (4.11) and (4.12) results in

$$X = X'(1 - V^2/c^2)^{1/2} = X'/\gamma. \qquad (4.13)$$

This says that the length of a moving object as measured in a stationary reference frame (X) is *less* than the actual length of the object as measured in its own reference frame (X'). This reduction in length is called the Lorentz contraction.

Note that the Lorentz contraction only occurs in the direction of motion. The dimensions of a moving object perpendicular to the motion remain unchanged.

4.6 Twin Paradox

An interesting application of time dilation is the so-called *twin paradox*, which turns out not to be a paradox at all. Two twins are initially the same age. One twin travels to a distant star on an interstellar spaceship which moves at speed V, which is close to the speed of light. Upon reaching the star, the traveling twin immediately turns around and heads home. When reaching home, the traveling twin has aged less than the twin that stayed home. This is easily explained by the time dilation effect, which shows that the proper time elapsed along the world line of the traveling twin is $(1 - V^2/c^2)^{1/2}$ times the proper time elapsed along the world line of the other twin.

The "paradox" part of the twin paradox arises from making the symmetric argument in which one assumes the reference frame of the traveling twin to be stationary. The frame of the earth-bound twin must then travel in the sense

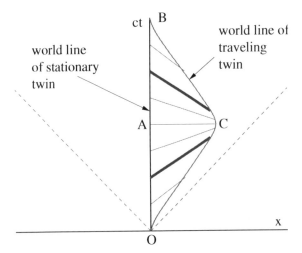

Figure 4.9: Definition sketch for the twin paradox. The vertical line is the world line of the twin that stays at home, while the traveling twin has the curved world line to the right. The slanted lines between the world lines are lines of simultaneity at various times for the traveling twin. The heavy lines of simultaneity bound the period during which the traveling twin is decelerating to a stop and accelerating toward home.

opposite that of the erstwhile traveling twin, which means that the earth-bound twin must age less rather than more. This substitution is justified on the basis of the principle of relativity, which states that the laws of physics must be the same in all inertial reference frames.

However, the above argument is fallacious, because the reference frame of the traveling twin is *not* inertial throughout the entire trip, since at various points the spaceship has to accelerate and decelerate. Thus, the principle of relativity cannot be used to assert the equivalence of the traveler's reference frame to the stationary frame.

Of particular importance is the period of deceleration and acceleration near the distant star. During this interval, the line of simulaneity of the traveling twin rotates, as illustrated in figure 4.9, such that the twin staying at home rapidly ages in the reference frame of the traveler. Thus, even though the acceleration of the traveling twin may occupy only a negligible segment of the twin's world line, the overall effect is not negligible. In fact, the shorter and more intense the period of acceleration, the more rapidly the earth-bound twin ages in the traveling frame during this interval!

4.7 Problems

1. Sketch your personal world line on a spacetime diagram for the last 24 hours, labeling by time and location special events such as meals, physics classes, etc. Relate the slope of the world line at various times to how fast you were walking, riding in a car, etc.

2. Spacetime conversions:

   (a) What is the distance from New York to Los Angeles in seconds? From here to the moon? From here to the sun?

   (b) What is one nanosecond in meters? One second? One day? One year?

3. Three events have the following spacetime coordinates: A is at $(x, ct) = (2\text{ m}, 1\text{ m})$; B is at $(x, ct) = (-2\text{ m}, 0\text{ m})$; C is at $(x, ct) = (0\text{ m}, 3\text{ m})$.

   (a) A world line for an object passes through events B and C. How fast and in which direction is the object moving?

   (b) A line of simultaneity for a coordinate system passes through events A and B. How fast and in which direction is the coordinate system moving?

   (c) What is the invariant interval between events A and B? B and C? A and C?

   (d) Can a signal from event B reach event A? Can it reach event C? Explain.

   Hint: Draw a spacetime diagram with all the events plotted before trying to answer the above questions.

4. In the following problem be sure to indicate the slope of all pertinent lines drawn.

   (a) In a spacetime diagram, sketch a line of simultaneity for a reference frame moving to the left at $V = c/2$, where c is the speed of light.

(b) Sketch the world line of an object which is initially stationary, but which accelerates to a velocity of $v = c/3$.

5. If the slopes of the world lines of the observers in the right panel of figure 4.6 are both $1/\beta$, find the slope of their line of simultaneity, AB.

6. Suppose that an interstellar spaceship goes a distance $X = 100$ light years relative to the rest frame in $T' = 10$ years of its own time.

   (a) Draw a spacetime diagram in the rest frame showing X, T', and the time T needed for this journey relative to the rest frame.

   (b) Compute T, using your spacetime diagram as an aid.

   (c) Compute the speed of the spaceship.

7. If an airline pilot flies 80 hr per month (in the rest frame) at 300 m s^{-1} for 30 years, how much younger will she be than her twin brother (who handles baggage) when she retires? Hint: Use $(1 + \epsilon)^x \approx 1 + x\epsilon$ for small ϵ.

8. A mu particle normally lives about 2×10^{-6} sec before it decays. However, muons created by cosmic rays 20 km up in the atmosphere reach the Earth's surface. How fast must they be going?

9. The Stanford Linear Accelerator accelerates electrons to a speed such that the 3 km long accelerator appears to be 8 cm long to the electron, due to the Lorentz contraction. How much less than the speed of light is the electron traveling? Hint: It is best to first develop an approximation for the relationship between $\gamma = (1 - v^2/c^2)^{-1/2}$ and the *difference* between c and v for a particle moving close to the speed of light.

10. How fast do you have to go to reach the center of our galaxy in your expected lifetime? At this speed, what does this distance appear to be? (We are about 30000 light years from the galactic center.)

11. Two identical spaceships pass each other going in the opposite direction at the same speed.

    (a) Sketch a spacetime diagram showing the world lines of the front and rear of each spaceship as well as lines of simultaneity for each spaceship.

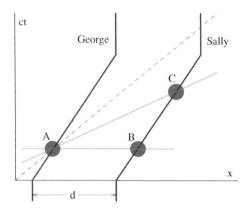

Figure 4.10: Sketch for moving twins. Line AC is the line of simultaneity for a reference frame moving with Sally and George.

   (b) Indicate an interval on the diagram corresponding to the rightward-moving spaceship's length in its own reference frame.

   (c) Indicate an interval corresponding to the leftward-moving spaceship's length in the reference frame of the rightward-moving spaceship.

   (d) Indicate an interval equal to the length of either spaceship in the rest frame.

12. George and Sally are twins initially separated by a distance d and at rest. In the rest frame they are initially the same age. At time $t = 0$ both George and Sally get in their spaceships and head to the right at velocity U. Both move a distance d to the right and decelerate to a halt. (See figure 4.10.)

   (a) When both are moving, how far away is Sally according to George?

   (b) How much older or younger is Sally relative to George while both are moving?

   (c) How much older or younger is Sally relative to George after both stop?

   Hint: Draw the triangle ABC in a reference frame moving with George and Sally.

Chapter 5

Applications of Special Relativity

In this chapter we continue the study of special relativity. Three important applications of the ideas developed in the previous chapter are made here. First, we show how to describe waves in the context of spacetime. We then see how waves which have no preferred reference frame (such as that of a medium supporting them) are constrained by special relativity to have a dispersion relation of a particular form. This dispersion relation turns out to be that of the relativistic matter waves of quantum mechanics. Second, we investigate the Doppler shift phenomenon, in which the frequency of a wave takes on different values in different coordinate systems. Third, we show how to add velocities in a relativistically consistent manner.

A new mathematical idea is presented in the context of relativistic waves, namely the spacetime vector or four-vector. Writing the laws of physics totally in terms of relativistic scalars and four-vectors insures that they will be valid in all inertial reference frames.

5.1 Waves in Spacetime

We now look at the characteristics of waves in spacetime. Recall that a sine wave moving to the right in one space dimension can be represented by

$$A(x,t) = A_0 \sin(kx - \omega t), \tag{5.1}$$

where A_0 is the (constant) amplitude of the wave, k is the wavenumber, and ω is the angular frequency, and that the quantity $\phi = kx - \omega t$ is called the

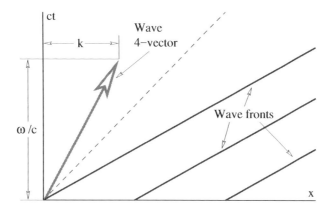

Figure 5.1: Sketch of wave fronts for a wave in spacetime. The large arrow is the associated wave four-vector, which has slope ω/ck. The slope of the wave fronts is the inverse, ck/ω. The phase speed of the wave is greater than c in this example. (Can you tell why?)

---

phase of the wave. For a plane wave in three space dimensions, the wave is represented in a similar way,

$$A(\mathbf{x}, t) = A_0 \sin(\mathbf{k} \cdot \mathbf{x} - \omega t), \tag{5.2}$$

where $\mathbf{x}$ is now the position vector and $\mathbf{k}$ is the wave vector. The magnitude of the wave vector, $|\mathbf{k}| = k$ is just the wavenumber of the wave and the direction of this vector indicates the direction the wave is moving. The phase of the wave in this case is $\phi = \mathbf{k} \cdot \mathbf{x} - \omega t$.

In the case of a one-dimensional wave moving to the right $\phi = kx - \omega t$. A wave front has constant phase ϕ, so solving this equation for t and multiplying by c, the speed of light in a vacuum, gives us an equation for the world line of a wave front:

$$ct = \frac{ckx}{\omega} - \frac{c\phi}{\omega} = \frac{cx}{u_p} - \frac{c\phi}{\omega} \quad \text{(wave front)}. \tag{5.3}$$

The slope of the world line in a spacetime diagram is the coefficient of x, or c/u_p, where $u_p = \omega/k$ is the phase speed. The world lines of the wave fronts of a wave are illustrated in figure 5.1.

5.2   Math Tutorial – Four-Vectors

Also shown in figure 5.1 is a spacetime vector or *four-vector* which represents the frequency and wavenumber of the wave, which we refer to as the *wave four-vector*. It is called a four-vector because it has 3 spacelike components and one timelike component when there are 3 space dimensions. In the case shown, there is only a single space dimension. The spacelike component of the wave four-vector is just k (or $\mathbf{k}$ when there are 3 space dimensions), while the timelike component is ω/c. The c is in the denominator to give the timelike component the same dimensions as the spacelike component. From figure 5.1 it is clear that the slope of the line representing the four-vector is ω/ck, which is just the inverse of the slope of the wave fronts.

Let us define some terminology. We indicate a four-vector by underlining and write the components in the following way: $\underline{k} = (k, \omega/c)$, where $\underline{k}$ is the wave four-vector, k is its spacelike component, and ω/c is its timelike component. For three space dimensions, where we have a wave vector rather than just a wavenumber, we write $\underline{k} = (\mathbf{k}, \omega/c)$.

Another example of a four-vector is simply the position vector in spacetime, $\underline{x} = (x, ct)$, or $\underline{x} = (\mathbf{x}, ct)$ in three space dimensions. The c *multiplies* the timelike component in this case, because that is what is needed to give it the same dimensions as the spacelike component.

In three dimensions we define a vector as a quantity with magnitude and direction. Extending this to spacetime, a four-vector is a quantity with magnitude and direction *in spacetime*. Implicit in this definition is the notion that the vector's magnitude is a quantity independent of coordinate system or reference frame. We have seen that the invariant interval in spacetime from the origin to the point (x, ct) is $I = (x^2 - c^2t^2)^{1/2}$, so it makes sense to identify this as the magnitude of the position vector. This leads to a way of defining a dot product of four-vectors. Given two four-vectors $\underline{A} = (\mathbf{A}, A_t)$ and $\underline{B} = (\mathbf{B}, B_t)$, the dot product is

$$\underline{A} \cdot \underline{B} = \mathbf{A} \cdot \mathbf{B} - A_t B_t \quad \text{(dot product in spacetime)}. \qquad (5.4)$$

This is consistent with the definition of invariant interval if we set $\underline{A} = \underline{B} = \underline{x}$, since then $\underline{x} \cdot \underline{x} = x^2 - c^2t^2 = I^2$.

In the odd geometry of spacetime it is not obvious what "perpendicular" means. We therefore *define* two four-vectors $\underline{A}$ and $\underline{B}$ to be perpendicular if their dot product is zero, $\underline{A} \cdot \underline{B} = 0$, in analogy with ordinary vectors.

The dot product of two four-vectors is a *scalar* result, i. e., its value is independent of coordinate system. This can be used to our advantage on occasion. For instance, consider the dot product of a four-vector $\underline{A}$ which resolves into (A_x, A_t) in the unprimed frame. Let us further suppose that the spacelike component is zero in some primed frame, so that the components in this frame are $(0, A'_t)$. The fact that the dot product is independent of coordinate system means that

$$\underline{A} \cdot \underline{A} = A_x^2 - A_t^2 = -A_t'^2. \tag{5.5}$$

This constitutes an extension of the spacetime Pythagorean theorem to four-vectors other than the position four-vector. Thus, for instance, the wavenumber for some wave may be zero in the primed frame, which means that the wavenumber and frequency in the unprimed frame are related to the frequency in the primed frame by

$$k^2 - \omega^2/c^2 = -\omega'^2/c^2. \tag{5.6}$$

5.3 Principle of Relativity Applied

Returning to the phase of a wave, we immediately see that

$$\phi = \mathbf{k} \cdot \mathbf{x} - \omega t = \mathbf{k} \cdot \mathbf{x} - (\omega/c)(ct) = \underline{k} \cdot \underline{x}. \tag{5.7}$$

Thus, a compact way to rewrite equation (5.2) is

$$A(\underline{x}) = A_0 \sin(\underline{k} \cdot \underline{x}). \tag{5.8}$$

Since $\underline{x}$ is known to be a four-vector and since the phase of a wave is known to be a scalar independent of reference frame, it follows that $\underline{k}$ is also a four-vector rather than just a set of numbers. Thus, the square of the length of the wave four-vector must also be a scalar independent of reference frame:

$$\underline{k} \cdot \underline{k} = \mathbf{k} \cdot \mathbf{k} - \omega^2/c^2 = const. \tag{5.9}$$

Let us review precisely what this means. As figure 5.2 shows, we can resolve a position four-vector into components in two different reference frames, $\underline{x} = (X, cT) = (X', cT')$. However, even though $X \neq X'$ and $T \neq T'$, the vector lengths computed from these two sets of components are necessarily the same: $\underline{x} \cdot \underline{x} = X^2 - c^2T^2 = X'^2 - c^2T'^2$.

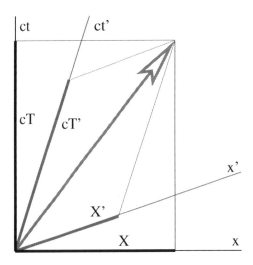

Figure 5.2: Resolution of a four-vector into components in two different reference frames.

Applying this to the wave four-vector, we infer that

$$k^2 - \omega^2/c^2 = k'^2 - \omega'^2/c^2 = const., \qquad (5.10)$$

where the unprimed and primed values of k and ω refer to the components of the wave four-vector in two different reference frames.

Up to now, this argument applies to *any* wave. However, waves can be divided into two categories, those for which a "special" reference frame exists, and those for which there is no such special frame. As an example of the former, sound waves look simplest in the reference frame in which the gas carrying the sound is stationary. The same is true of light propagating through a material medium with an index of refraction not equal to unity. In both cases the speed of the wave is the same in all directions *only* in the frame in which the material medium is stationary.

Suppose we have a machine that produces a wave with wavenumber k and frequency ω in its own rest frame. If we observe the wave from a moving reference frame, the wavenumber and frequency will be different, say, k' and ω'. However, these quantities will be related by equation (5.10).

Up to this point the argument applies to *any* wave whether a special reference frame exists or not; the observed changes in wavenumber and frequency have nothing to do with the wave itself, but are just consequences of how we have chosen to observe it. However, if there is no special reference frame for the type of wave under consideration, then the same result can be obtained by keeping the observer stationary and moving the wave-producing machine in the opposite direction. By moving it at various speeds, any desired value of k' can be obtained *in the initial reference frame* (as opposed to some other frame), and the resulting value of ω' can be computed using equation (5.10).

This is actually an amazing result. We have shown on the basis of the principle of relativity that any wave type for which no special reference frame exists can be made to take on a full range of frequencies and wavenumbers in any given reference frame, and furthermore that these frequencies and wavenumbers obey

$$\omega^2 = k^2 c^2 + \mu^2. \tag{5.11}$$

Equation (5.11) comes from solving equation (5.10) for ω^2 and the constant μ^2 equals the constant in equation (5.10) times $-c^2$. Equation (5.11) relates frequency to wavenumber and therefore is the *dispersion relation* for such waves. We call waves which have no special reference frame and therefore necessarily obey equation (5.11) *relativistic waves*. The only difference in the dispersion relations between different types of relativistic waves is the value of the constant μ. The meaning of this constant will become clear later.

5.4 Characteristics of Relativistic Waves

Light in a vacuum is an example of a wave for which no special reference frame exists. For light, $\mu = 0$, and we have (taking the positive root) $\omega = ck$. This simply states what we know already, namely that the phase speed of light in a vacuum is c.

If $\mu \neq 0$, waves of this type are dispersive. The phase speed is

$$u_p = \frac{\omega}{k} = (c^2 + \mu^2/k^2)^{1/2}. \tag{5.12}$$

This phase speed always exceeds c, which at first seems like an unphysical conclusion. However, the group velocity of the wave is

$$u_g = \frac{d\omega}{dk} = \frac{c^2 k}{(k^2 c^2 + \mu^2)^{1/2}} = \frac{kc^2}{\omega} = \frac{c^2}{u_p}, \tag{5.13}$$

which is always less than c. Since wave packets and hence signals propagate at the group velocity, waves of this type are physically reasonable even though the phase speed exceeds the speed of light.

Another interesting property of such waves is that the wave four-vector is parallel to the world line of a wave packet in spacetime. This is easily shown by the following argument. As figure 5.1 shows, the spacelike component of a wave four-vector is k, while the timelike component is ω/c. The slope of the four-vector on a spacetime diagram is therefore ω/kc. However, the slope of the world line of a wave packet moving with group velocity u_g is $c/u_g = \omega/(kc)$, which is the same as the slope of the $\underline{k}$ four-vector.

Note that when $k = 0$ we have $\omega = \mu$. In this case the group velocity of the wave is zero. For this reason we call μ the *rest frequency* of the wave.

5.5 The Doppler Shift

You have probably heard how the pitch of a train horn changes as it passes you. When the train is approaching, the pitch or frequency is higher than when it is moving away from you. This is called the Doppler shift. A similar, but distinct shift occurs if you are moving past a source of sound. If a stationary whistle is blowing, the pitch perceived from a moving car is higher while moving toward the source than when moving away. The first case thus has a *moving source*, while the second case has a *moving observer*.

In this section we compute the Doppler shift as it applies to light moving through a vacuum. Figure 5.3 shows the geometry for computing the time between wave fronts of light for a stationary and a moving reference frame. The time in the stationary frame is just T. Since the world lines of the wave fronts have a slope of unity, the sides of the shaded triangle have the same value, X. If the observer is moving at speed U, the slope of the observer's world line is c/U, which means that $c/U = (cT + X)/X$. Solving this for X yields $X = UT/(1-U/c)$, which can then be used to compute $T' = T + X/c = T/(1 - U/c)$. This formula as it stands leads to the classical Doppler shift for a moving observer. However, with relativistic velocities, one additional factor needs to be taken into account: The observer experiences time dilation since he or she is moving. The actual time measured by the observer between wave fronts is actually

$$\tau = (T'^2 - X^2/c^2)^{1/2} = T\frac{(1 - U^2/c^2)^{1/2}}{1 - U/c} = T\left(\frac{1 + U/c}{1 - U/c}\right)^{1/2}, \qquad (5.14)$$

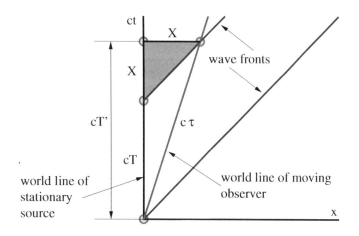

Figure 5.3: Definition sketch for computing the Doppler shift for light.

where the last step uses $1 - U^2/c^2 = (1 - U/c)(1 + U/c)$. From this we infer the relativistic Doppler shift formula for light in a vacuum:

$$\omega' = \omega \left(\frac{1 - U/c}{1 + U/c} \right)^{1/2}, \tag{5.15}$$

where the frequency measured by the moving observer is $\omega' = 2\pi/\tau$ and the frequency observed in the stationary frame is $\omega = 2\pi/T$.

We could go on to determine the Doppler shift resulting from a moving source. However, by the principle of relativity, the laws of physics should be the same in the reference frame in which the observer is stationary and the source is moving. Furthermore, the speed of light is still c in that frame. Therefore, the problem of a stationary observer and a moving source is conceptually the same as the problem of a moving observer and a stationary source when the wave is moving at speed c. This is unlike the case for, say, sound waves, where the stationary observer and the stationary source yield different formulas for the Doppler shift.

5.6 Addition of Velocities

Figure 5.4 shows the world line of a moving object from the point of view of two different reference frames, with the primed frame (left panel) moving to

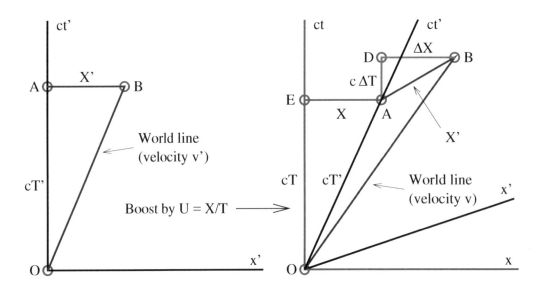

Figure 5.4: Definition sketch for relativistic velocity addition. The two panels show the world line of a moving object relative to two different reference frames moving at velocity U with respect to each other. The velocity of the world line in the left panel is v' while its velocity in the right panel is v.

the right at speed U relative to the unprimed frame (right panel). The goal is to calculate the velocity of the object relative to the unprimed frame, v, assuming its velocity in the primed frame, v' is known. The classical result is simply

$$v = U + v' \quad \text{(classical result)}. \tag{5.16}$$

However, this is inconsistent with the speed of light being constant in all reference frames, since if we substitute c for v', this formula predicts that the speed of light in the unprimed frame is $U + c$.

We can use the geometry of figure 5.4 to come up with the correct relativistic formula. From the right panel of this figure we infer that

$$\frac{v}{c} = \frac{X + \Delta X}{cT + c\Delta T} = \frac{X/(cT) + \Delta X/(cT)}{1 + \Delta T/T}. \tag{5.17}$$

This follows from the fact that the slope of the world line of the object in this frame is c/v. The slope is calculated as the ratio of the rise, $c(T + \Delta T)$, to the run, $X + \Delta X$.

From the left panel of figure 5.4 we similarly see that

$$\frac{v'}{c} = \frac{X'}{cT'}.$$ (5.18)

However, we can apply our calculations of Lorentz contraction and time dilation from the previous chapter to triangles ABD and OAE in the right panel. The slope of AB is U/c because AB is horizontal in the left panel, so $X' = \Delta X (1 - U^2/c^2)^{1/2}$. Similarly, the slope of OA is c/U since OA is vertical in the left panel, and $T' = T(1 - U^2/c^2)^{1/2}$. Substituting these formulas into the equation for v'/c yields

$$\frac{v'}{c} = \frac{\Delta X}{cT}.$$ (5.19)

Again using what we know about the triangles ABD and OAE, we see that

$$\frac{U}{c} = \frac{c\Delta T}{\Delta X} = \frac{X}{cT}.$$ (5.20)

Finally, we calculate $\Delta T/T$ by noticing that

$$\frac{\Delta T}{T} = \frac{\Delta T}{T} \frac{c\Delta X}{c\Delta X} = \left(\frac{c\Delta T}{\Delta X}\right)\left(\frac{\Delta X}{cT}\right) = \frac{U}{c}\frac{v'}{c}.$$ (5.21)

Substituting equations (5.19), (5.20), and (5.21) into equation (5.17) and simplifying yields the relativistic velocity addition formula:

$$v = \frac{U + v'}{1 + Uv'/c^2} \quad \text{(special relativity)}.$$ (5.22)

Notice how this equation behaves in various limits. If $|Uv'| \ll c^2$, the denominator of equation (5.22) is nearly unity, and the special relativistic formula reduces to the classical case. On the other hand, if $v' = c$, then equation (5.22) reduces to $v = c$. In other words, if the object in question is moving at the speed of light in one reference frame, it is moving at the speed of light in all reference frames, i. e., for all possible values of U. Thus, we have found a velocity addition formula that 1) reduces to the classical formula for low velocities and 2) gives the observed results for very high velocities as well.

Equation (5.22) is valid even if v' is negative, i. e., if the object is moving to the right less rapidly than the primed reference frame, or even if it is moving to the left in the unprimed frame.

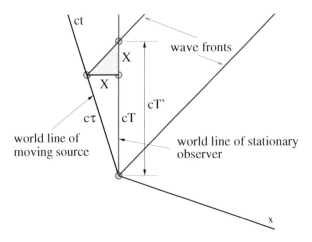

Figure 5.5: Doppler shift for a moving light source.

5.7   Problems

1. Sketch the wave fronts and the $\underline{k}$ four-vector in a spacetime diagram for the case where $\omega/k = 2c$. Label your axes and space the wave fronts correctly for the case $k = 4\pi \text{ m}^{-1}$.

2. If the four-vector $\underline{k} = (0, 1 \text{ nm}^{-1})$ in the rest frame, find the space and time components of $\underline{k}$ in a frame moving to the *left* at speed $c/2$.

3. Let's examine the four-vector $\underline{u} = (u_g, c)/(1 - \beta^2)^{1/2}$ where $\beta = u_g/c$, u_g being the velocity of some object. The four-vector $\underline{u}$ is called the four-velocity.

   (a) Show that $\underline{u}$ is parallel to the world line of the object.

   (b) Show that $\underline{u} \cdot \underline{u} = -c^2$.

   (c) If u_g is the group velocity of a relativistic wave packet, show that $\underline{k} = (\mu/c^2)\underline{u}$, where $\underline{k}$ is the central wave four-vector of the wave packet.

4. Find the Doppler shift for a moving source of light from figure 5.5, roughly following the procedure used in the text to find the shift for a moving observer. (Assume that the source moves to the left at speed

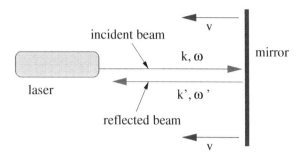

Figure 5.6: Laser beam reflecting off of a moving mirror.

U.) Is the result the same as for the moving observer, as demanded by the principle of relativity?

5. Find the Doppler shift for a stationary source of *sound* ($c \approx 380$ m s^{-1} in a stationary atmosphere) as measured by a moving observer. Follow the procedure as for light in section 5.5 except note that the proper time τ is virtually the same as the time T' in figure 5.3 since speeds are much less than the speed of light.

6. Suppose you shine a laser with frequency ω and wavenumber k on a mirror moving toward you at speed v, as seen in figure 5.6. What are the frequency ω' and wavenumber k' of the reflected beam? Hint: Find the frequency of the incident beam in the reference frame of the mirror. The frequency of the reflected beam will be the same as that of the incident beam in this frame. Then transform back to the reference frame of the laser.

7. Suppose the moving twin in the twin paradox has a powerful telescope so that she can watch her twin brother back on earth during the entire trip. Describe how the earthbound twin appears to age to the travelling twin compared to her own rate of aging. Use a spacetime diagram to illustrate your argument and consider separately the outbound and return legs. Remember that light travels at the speed of light! Hint: Does the concept of Doppler shift help here?

8. Find the velocity of an object with respect to the rest frame if it is

moving at a velocity of $0.1c$ with respect to another frame which itself is moving in the same direction at $0.1c$ relative to the rest frame using

(a) the Galilean formula and

(b) the formula of special relativity.

Determine the fractional error made in using the Galilean formula.

9. Each stage of a high performance 3 stage rocket can accelerate to a speed of $0.9c$ from rest. If the rocket starts from rest, how fast does the final stage eventually go?

10. An interstellar spaceship is going from Earth to Sirius with speed $U = 0.8c$ relative to the rest frame. It passes a spaceship which is going from Sirius to Earth at a speed of $0.95c$ in the reference frame of the first spaceship. What is the velocity (direction and speed) of the second spaceship in the rest frame?

Chapter 6

Acceleration and General Relativity

General relativity is Einstein's extension of special relativity to include gravity. An important aspect of general relativity is that spacetime is no longer necessarily flat, but in fact may be curved under the influence of mass. Understanding curved spacetime is an advanced topic which is not easily accessible at the level of this text. However, it turns out that some insight into general relativistic phenomena may be obtained by investigating the effects of acceleration in the flat (but non-Euclidean) space of special relativity.

The central assumption of general relativity is the equivalence principle, which states that gravity is a force which arises from being in an accelerated reference frame. To understand this we must first investigate the concept of acceleration. We then see how this leads to phenomena such as the gravitational red shift, event horizons, and black holes. We also introduce in a preliminary way the notions of force and mass.

6.1   Acceleration

Imagine that you are in a powerful luxury car stopped at a stoplight. As you sit there, gravity pushes you into the comfortable leather seat. The light turns green and you "floor it". The car accelerates and an additional force pushes you into the seat back. You round a curve, and yet another force pushes you toward the outside of the curve. (But the well designed seat and seat belt keep you from feeling discomfort!)

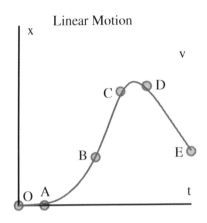

Figure 6.1: Example of linear motion.

Let us examine the idea of *acceleration* more closely. Considering first acceleration in one dimension, figure 6.1 shows the position of an object as a function of time, $x(t)$. The velocity is simply the time rate of change of the position:

$$v(t) = \frac{dx(t)}{dt}. \tag{6.1}$$

The acceleration is the time rate of change of velocity:

$$a(t) = \frac{dv(t)}{dt} = \frac{d^2x(t)}{dt^2}. \tag{6.2}$$

In figure 6.1, only the segment OA has zero velocity. Velocity is increasing in AB, and the acceleration is positive there. Velocity is constant in BC, which means that the acceleration is zero. Velocity is decreasing in CD, and the acceleration is negative. Finally, in DE, the velocity is negative and the acceleration is zero.

In two or three dimensions, position **x**, velocity **v**, and acceleration **a** are all vectors, so that the velocity is

$$\mathbf{v}(t) = \frac{d\mathbf{x}(t)}{dt} \tag{6.3}$$

while the acceleration is

$$\mathbf{a}(t) = \frac{d\mathbf{v}(t)}{dt}. \tag{6.4}$$

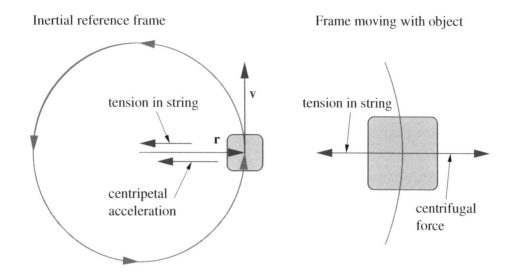

Figure 6.2: Two different views of circular motion of an object. The left panel shows the view from the inertial reference frame at rest with the center of the circle. The tension in the string is the only force and it causes an acceleration toward the center of the circle. The right panel shows the view from an accelerated frame in which the object is at rest. In this frame the tension in the string balances the centrifugal force, which is the inertial force arising from being in an accelerated reference frame, leaving zero net force.

Thus, over some short time interval Δt, the changes in $\mathbf{x}$ and $\mathbf{v}$ can be written

$$\Delta \mathbf{x} = \mathbf{v}\Delta t \qquad \Delta \mathbf{v} = \mathbf{a}\Delta t. \tag{6.5}$$

These are vector equations, so the subtractions implied by the "delta" operations must be done vectorially. An example where the vector nature of these quantities is important is motion in a circle at constant speed, which is discussed in the next section.

6.2 Circular Motion

Imagine an object constrained by an attached string to move in a circle at constant speed, as shown in the left panel of figure 6.2. We now demonstrate

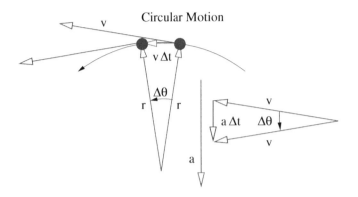

Figure 6.3: Definition sketch for computing centripetal acceleration.

that the acceleration of the object is toward the center of the circle. The acceleration in this special case is called the *centripetal acceleration*.

Figure 6.3 shows the position of the object at two times spaced by the time interval Δt. The position vector of the object relative to the center of the circle rotates through an angle $\Delta\theta$ during this interval, so the angular rate of revolution of the object about the center is $\omega = \Delta\theta/\Delta t$. The magnitude of the velocity of the object is v, so the object moves a distance $v\Delta t$ during the time interval. To the extent that this distance is small compared to the radius r of the circle, the angle $\Delta\theta = v\Delta t/r$. Solving for v and using $\omega = \Delta\theta/\Delta t$, we see that

$$v = \omega r \quad \text{(circular motion)}. \tag{6.6}$$

The direction of the velocity vector changes over this interval, even though the magnitude v stays the same. Figure 6.3 shows that this change in direction implies an acceleration a which is directed toward the center of the circle, as noted above. The magnitude of the vectoral change in velocity in the time interval Δt is $a\Delta t$. Since the angle between the initial and final velocities is the same as the angle $\Delta\theta$ between the initial and final radius vectors, we see from the geometry of the triangle in figure 6.3 that $a\Delta t/v = \Delta\theta$. Solving for a results in

$$a = \omega v \quad \text{(circular motion)}. \tag{6.7}$$

Combining equations (6.6) and (6.7) yields the equation for centripetal acceleration:

$$a = \omega^2 r = v^2/r \quad \text{(centripetal acceleration)}. \tag{6.8}$$

The second form is obtained by eliminating ω from the first form using equation (6.6).

6.3 Acceleration, Force, and Mass

We have a good intuitive feel for the concepts of force and mass because they are very much a part of our everyday experience. We think of force as how hard we push on something. Mass is the resistance of an object to acceleration if it is otherwise free to move. Thus, pushing on a bicycle on a smooth, level road causes it to accelerate more readily than pushing on a car. We say that the car has greater mass. We can summarize this relationship with Newton's second law

$$F = ma \tag{6.9}$$

where F is the total force on an object, m is its mass, and a is the acceleration resulting from the force.

Three provisos apply to equation (6.9). First, it only makes sense in unmodified form when the velocity of the object is much less than the speed of light. For relativistic velocities it is best to write this equation in a slightly different form which we introduce later. Second, the force must be the total force, including all frictional and other incidental forces which might otherwise be neglected by an uncritical observer. Third, it only works in a reference frame which itself is unaccelerated, i.e., an *inertial reference frame*. We deal below with accelerated reference frames.

6.4 Acceleration in Special Relativity

As noted above, acceleration is just the time rate of change of velocity. We use the above results to determine how acceleration transforms from one reference frame to another. Figure 6.4 shows the world line of an *accelerated reference frame*, with a time-varying velocity $U(t)$ relative to the unprimed inertial rest frame. Defining $\Delta U = U(T) - U(0)$ as the change in the velocity of the accelerated frame (relative to the unprimed frame) between events A and C, we can relate this to the change of velocity, $\Delta U'$, of the accelerated

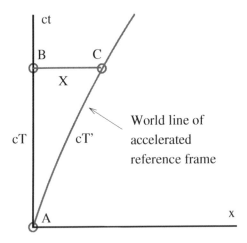

Figure 6.4: World line of the origin of an accelerated reference frame.

frame *relative to an inertial frame moving with the initial velocity, $U(0)$.* Applying the equation for the relativistic addition of velocities, we find

$$U(T) = U(0) + \Delta U = \frac{U(0) + \Delta U'}{1 + U(0)\Delta U'/c^2}. \tag{6.10}$$

We now note that the mean acceleration of the reference frame between events A and C in the rest frame is just $a = \Delta U/T$, whereas the mean acceleration in the primed frame between the same two events is $a' = \Delta U'/T'$. From equation (6.10) we find that

$$\Delta U = \frac{\Delta U'[1 - U(0)^2/c^2]}{1 + U(0)\Delta U'/c^2}, \tag{6.11}$$

and the acceleration of the primed reference frame as it appears in the unprimed frame is

$$a = \frac{\Delta U}{T} = \frac{\Delta U'[1 - U(0)^2/c^2]}{T[1 + U(0)\Delta U'/c^2]}. \tag{6.12}$$

Since we are interested in the instantaneous rather than the average acceleration, we let T become small. This has three consequences. First, ΔU and $\Delta U'$ become small, which means that the term $U(0)\Delta U'/c^2$ in the denominator of equation (6.12) can be ignored compared to 1. This means that

$$a \approx \frac{\Delta U'[1 - U(0)^2/c^2]}{T}, \quad (6.13)$$

with the approximation becoming exact as $T \to 0$. Second, the "triangle" with the curved side in figure 6.4 becomes a true triangle, with the result that $T' = T[1 - U(0)^2/c^2]^{1/2}$. The acceleration of the primed frame with respect to an inertial frame moving at speed $U(0)$ can therefore be written

$$a' = \frac{\Delta U'}{T'} = \frac{\Delta U'}{T[1 - U(0)^2/c^2]^{1/2}}. \quad (6.14)$$

Third, we can replace $U(0)$ with U, since the velocity of the accelerated frame doesn't change very much over a short time interval.

Dividing equation (6.13) by equation (6.14) results in a relationship between the two accelerations:

$$a = a'(1 - U^2/c^2)^{3/2}, \quad (6.15)$$

which shows that the acceleration of a rapidly moving object, a, as observed from the rest frame, is less than its acceleration relative to an inertial reference frame in which the object is nearly stationary, a', by the factor $(1 - U^2/c^2)^{3/2}$. We call this latter acceleration the *intrinsic acceleration*. This difference in observed acceleration between the two inertial reference frames is purely the result of the geometry of spacetime, but it has interesting consequences.

Identifying a with dU/dt, we can integrate the acceleration equation assuming that the intrinsic acceleration a' is constant and that the velocity $U = 0$ at time $t = 0$. We get the following result (verify this by differentiating with respect to time):

$$a't = \frac{U}{(1 - U^2/c^2)^{1/2}}, \quad (6.16)$$

which may be solved for U/c:

$$\frac{U}{c} = \frac{a't/c}{[1 + (a't/c)^2]^{1/2}}. \quad (6.17)$$

This is plotted in figure 6.5. Classically, the velocity U would reach the speed of light when $a't/c = 1$. However, as figure 6.5 shows, the rate at which the

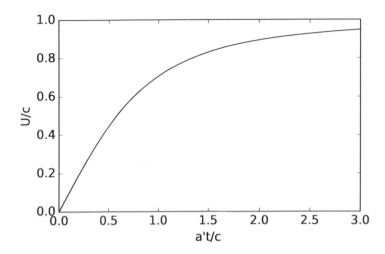

Figure 6.5: Velocity divided by the speed of light as a function of the product of the time and the (constant) acceleration divided by the speed of light.

---

velocity increases with time slows as the object moves faster, such that U approaches c asymptotically, but never reaches it.

The results for this section are valid only for acceleration components in the direction of motion. The components perpendicular to this direction behave differently and are treated in more advanced texts.

6.5   Accelerated Reference Frames

Referring back to the forces being felt by the occupant of a car, it is clear that the forces associated with accelerations are directed opposite the accelerations and proportional to their magnitudes. For instance, when accelerating away from a stoplight, the acceleration is forward and the perceived force is backward. When turning a corner, the acceleration is toward the corner while the perceived force is away from the corner. Such forces are called *inertial forces*.

The origin of these forces can be understood by determining how acceleration changes when one observes it from a reference frame which is itself accelerated. Suppose that the primed reference frame is accelerating to the right with acceleration A relative to the unprimed frame. The position x' in the primed frame can be related to the position x in the unprimed frame by

$$x = x' + X, \tag{6.18}$$

where X is the position of the origin of the primed frame in the unprimed frame. Taking the second time derivative, we see that

$$a = a' + A, \tag{6.19}$$

where $a = d^2x/dt^2$ is the acceleration in the unprimed frame and $a' = d^2x'/dt^2$ is the acceleration according to an observer in the primed frame.

We now substitute this into equation (6.9) and move the term involving A to the left side:

$$F - mA = ma'. \tag{6.20}$$

This shows that Newton's second law represented by equation (6.9) is not valid in an accelerated reference frame, because the total force F and the acceleration a' in this frame don't balance as they do in the unaccelerated frame; the additional term $-mA$ messes up this balance.

We can fix this problem by considering $-mA$ to be a type of force, in which case we can include it as a part of the total force F. This is the inertial force which we mentioned above. Thus, to summarize, we can make Newton's second law work when objects are observed from accelerated reference frames if we include as part of the total force an inertial force which is equal to $-mA$, A being the acceleration of the reference frame of the observer and m the mass of the object being observed.

The right panel of figure 6.2 shows the inertial force observed in the reference frame of an object moving in circular motion at constant speed. In the case of circular motion the inertial force is called the *centrifugal force*. It points away from the center of the circle and just balances the tension in the string. This makes the total force on the object zero in its own reference frame, which is necessary since the object cannot move (or accelerate) in this frame.

General relativity says that gravity is nothing more than an inertial force. This was called the *equivalence principle* by Einstein. Since the gravitational force on the Earth points downward, it follows that we must be constantly accelerating upward as we stand on the surface of the Earth! The obvious problem with this interpretation of gravity is that we don't appear to be

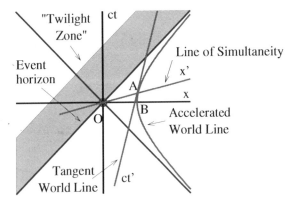

Figure 6.6: Spacetime diagram showing the world line of the origin of a reference frame undergoing constant acceleration.

moving away from the center of the Earth, which would seem to be a natural consequence of such an acceleration. However, relativity has a surprise in store for us here.

It follows from the above considerations that something can be learned about general relativity by examining the properties of accelerated reference frames. In particular, we can gain insight into the above apparent paradox. Equation (6.17) shows that the velocity of an object undergoing constant intrinsic acceleration a (note that we have dropped the "prime" from a to simplify the notation) is

$$v = \frac{dx}{dt} = \frac{at}{[1 + (at/c)^2]^{1/2}}, \tag{6.21}$$

where t is the time and c is the speed of light. A function $x(t)$ which satisfies equation (6.21) is

$$x(t) = (c^2/a)[1 + (at/c)^2]^{1/2}. \tag{6.22}$$

(Verify this by differentiating it.) The interval OB in figure 6.6 is of length $x(0) = c^2/A$.

The slanted line OA is a line of simultaneity associated with the unaccelerated world line tangent to the accelerated world line at point A. This line of simultaneity goes through the origin, as is shown in figure 6.6. To demonstrate this, multiply equations (6.21) and (6.22) together and solve for

v/c:

$$v/c = ct/x. \tag{6.23}$$

From figure 6.6 we see that ct/x is the slope of the line OA, where $(x,\ ct)$ are the coordinates of event A. Equation (6.23) shows that this line is indeed the desired line of simultaneity, since its slope is the inverse of the slope of the world line, c/v. Since there is nothing special about the event A, we infer that *all* lines of simultaneity associated with the accelerated world line pass through the origin.

We now inquire about the length of the invariant interval OA in figure 6.6. Recalling that $I^2 = x^2 - c^2t^2$ and using equation (6.22), we find that the length of OA is

$$I = (x^2 - c^2t^2)^{1/2} = (c^4/a^2)^{1/2} = c^2/a, \tag{6.24}$$

which is the same as the length of the interval OB. By extension, *all* events on the accelerated world line are the same invariant interval from the origin. Recalling that the interval along a line of simultaneity is the distance in the associated reference frame, we reach the astonishing conclusion that even though the object associated with the curved world line in figure 6.6 is accelerating away from the origin, it always remains the same distance (in its own frame) from the origin.

The analogy between this problem and the apparent paradox in which one remains a fixed distance from the center of the earth while accelerating away from it is not perfect. In particular, the earth case depends on the existence of the earth's mass.

6.6   Gravitational Red Shift

Light emitted at a lower level in a gravitational field has its frequency reduced as it travels to a higher level. This phenomenon is called the *gravitational red shift*. Figure 6.26 shows why this happens. Since experiencing a gravitational force is equivalent to being in an accelerated reference frame, we can use the tools of special relativity to view the process of light emission and absorption from the point of view of the unaccelerated or inertial frame. In this reference frame the observer of the light is accelerating to the right, as indicated by the curved world line in figure 6.26, which is equivalent to a gravitational force to the left. The light is emitted at point A with frequency ω by a source which

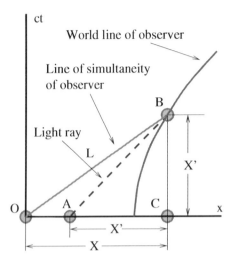

Figure 6.7: Spacetime diagram for explaining the gravitational red shift. Why is the interval AC equal to the interval BC? L is the length of the invariant interval OB.

is stationary at this instant. At this instant the observer is also stationary in this frame. However, by the time the light gets to the observer, he or she has a velocity to the right which means that the observer measures a Doppler shifted frequency ω' for the light. Since the observer is moving away from the source, $\omega' < \omega$, as indicated above.

The relativistic Doppler shift is given by

$$\frac{\omega'}{\omega} = \left(\frac{1 - U/c}{1 + U/c}\right)^{1/2}, \tag{6.25}$$

so we need to compute U/c. The line of simultaneity for the observer at point B goes through the origin, and is thus given by line segment OB in figure 6.26. The slope of this line is U/c, where U is the velocity of the observer at point B. From the figure we see that this slope is also given by the ratio X'/X. Equating these, eliminating X in favor of $L = (X^2 - X'^2)^{1/2} = c^2/g$, which is the actual invariant distance of the observer from the origin, and substituting into equation (6.25) results in our gravitational red shift formula:

$$\frac{\omega'}{\omega} = \left(\frac{X - X'}{X + X'}\right)^{1/2} = \left(\frac{(L^2 + X'^2)^{1/2} - X'}{(L^2 + X'^2)^{1/2} + X'}\right)^{1/2}. \tag{6.26}$$

If $X' = 0$, then there is no redshift, because the source is collocated with the observer. On the other hand, if the source is located at the origin, so $X' = X$, the Doppler shifted frequency is zero. In addition, the light never gets to the observer, since the world line is asymptotic to the light world line passing through the origin. If the source is at a higher level in the gravitational field than the observer, so that $X' < 0$, then the frequency is shifted to a higher value, i. e., it becomes a "blue shift".

Equation (6.26) works for more complex geometries than that associated with an accelerated reference frame, e.g., for the gravitational field g associated with a star, as long as $|X'| \ll c^2/g$. In this case L is no longer the distance to the center of the star but remains equal to c^2/g.

6.7   Event Horizons

The 45° diagonal line passing through the origin in figure 6.6 is called the *event horizon* for the accelerated observer in this figure. Notice that light from the "twilight zone" above and to the left of the event horizon cannot reach the accelerated observer. However, the reverse is not true — a light signal emitted to the left by the observer can cross the event horizon into the "twilight zone". The event horizon thus has a peculiar one-way character — it passes signals from right to left, but not from left to right.

6.8   Problems

1. An object moves as described in figure 6.8, which shows its position x as a function of time t.

   (a) Is the velocity positive, negative, or zero at each of the points A, B, C, D, E, and F?

   (b) Is the acceleration positive, negative, or zero at each of the points A, B, C, D, E, and F?

2. An object is moving counterclockwise at constant speed around the circle shown in figure 6.9 due to the fact that it is attached by a string to the center of the circle at point O.

   (a) Sketch the object's velocity vectors at points A, B, and C.

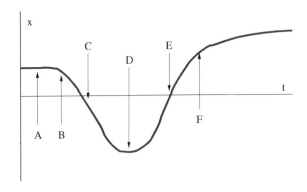

Figure 6.8: Position of an object as a function of time.

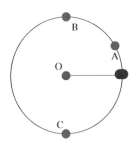

Figure 6.9: Object in circular motion.

(b) Sketch the object's acceleration vectors at points A, B, and C.

(c) If the string breaks at point A, sketch the subsequent trajectory followed by the object.

3. How fast are you going after accelerating from rest with intrinsic acceleration $a = 10$ m s^{-2} after the given times measured in the rest frame:

   (a) 10 y?

   (b) 100000 y?

Express your answer as the speed of light minus your actual speed. Hint: You may have a numerical problem on the second part, which you should try to resolve using the approximation $(1 + \epsilon)^x \approx 1 + x\epsilon$, which is valid for $|\epsilon| \ll 1$.

4. An object's world line is defined by $x(t) = (d^2 + c^2 t^2)^{1/2}$ where d is a constant and c is the speed of light.

   (a) Find the object's velocity as a function of time.

   (b) Using the above result, find the slope of the tangent to the world line as a function of time.

   (c) Find where the line of simultaneity corresponding to each tangent world line crosses the x axis.

5. A car accelerates in the positive x direction at 3 m s^{-2}.

   (a) What is the net force on a 100 kg man in the car as viewed from an inertial reference frame?

   (b) What is the inertial force experienced by this man in the reference frame of the car?

   (c) What is the net force experienced by the man in the car's (accelerated) reference frame?

6. A person is sitting in a comfortable chair in her home in Bogotá, Colombia, which is essentially on the equator.

   (a) What would the rotational period of the earth have to be to make this person weightless?

   (b) What is her acceleration according to the equivalence principle in the earth frame in this situation?

7. At time $t = 0$ a Zork (a creature from the planet Zorkheim) accelerating to the right at $a = 10^3 \text{ m s}^{-2}$ in a spaceship accidently drops its stopwatch from the spaceship just when its velocity is zero.

   (a) Describe qualitatively how the hands of the watch appear to move to the Zork as it observes the watch through a powerful telescope.

   (b) After a very long time what does the watch read?

   Hint: Draw a spacetime diagram with the world lines of the spaceship and the watch. Then send light rays from the watch to the spaceship.

8. Using a spacetime diagram, show why signals from events on the hidden side of the event horizon from an accelerating spaceship cannot reach the spaceship.

9. Approximate equation (6.26) to first order in X' for the case in which $X' \ll L$.

10. Imagine two identical clocks, one on top of the volcano Chimborazo in Ecuador (6300 m above sea level), the other in the Ecuadorian city of Guayaquil (at sea level).

    (a) From the perspective of Chimborazo, does the clock in Guayaquil appear to be running faster or slower than the Chimborazo clock? Explain.

    (b) Compute the fractional frequency difference $(\omega - \omega')/\omega$ in this case, where ω is the freqency of the Guayaquil clock as observed in Guayaquil (and the frequency of the Chimborazo clock on Chimborazo) and ω' is the frequency of the Guayaquil clock as observed from Chimborazo. You may wish to use the results of the previous problem.

Chapter 7

Matter Waves

We begin our study of quantum mechanics by discussing the diffraction undergone by X-rays and electrons when they interact with a crystal. X-rays are a form of electromagnetic radiation with wavelengths comparable to the distances between atoms. Scattering from atoms in a regular crystalline structure results in an interference pattern which is in many ways similar to the pattern from a diffraction grating. We first develop Bragg's law for diffraction of X-rays from a crystal. Two practical techniques for doing X-ray diffraction are then described.

It turns out that electrons have wave-like properties and also undergo Bragg diffraction by crystals. Bragg diffraction thus provides a crucial bridge between the worlds of waves and particles. With this bridge we introduce the classical ideas of momentum and energy by relating them to the wave vector and frequency of a wave. The properties of waves also give rise to the Heisenberg uncertainty principle.

Table 7.1 shows a table of the Nobel prizes associated with the ideas presented in this chapter. This gives us a feel for the chronology of these discoveries and indicates how important they were to the development of physics in the early 20th century.

7.1 Bragg's Law

Figure 7.1 schematically illustrates interference between waves scattering from two adjacent rows of atoms in a crystal. The net effect of scattering from a single row is equivalent to partial reflection from a mirror imagined to

Year	Recipient	Contribution
1901	W. K. Röntgen	Discovery of X-rays
1906	J. J. Thomson	Discovery of electron
1914	M. von Laue	X-ray diffraction in crystals
1915	W. and L. Bragg	X-ray analysis of crystal structure
1918	M. Planck	Energy quantization
1921	A. Einstein	Photoelectric effect
1922	N. Bohr	Structure of atoms
1929	L.-V. de Broglie	Wave nature of electrons
1932	W. Heisenberg	Quantum mechanics
1933	Schrödinger and Dirac	Atomic theory
1937	Davisson and Thomson	Electron diffraction in crystals

Table 7.1: Selected Nobel prize winners, year of award, and contribution.

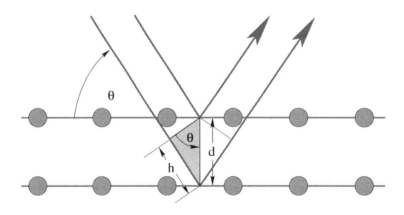

Figure 7.1: Schematic diagram for determining Bragg's law.

be aligned with the row. Thus, the angle of "reflection" equals the angle of incidence for each row. Interference then occurs between the beams reflecting off different rows of atoms in the crystal.

For the two adjacent rows shown in figure 7.1, the path difference between beams is $2h = 2d\sin\theta$. For constructive interference this must be an integer number of wavelengths, $m\lambda$, where the integer m is called the *order of interference*. The result is Bragg's law of diffraction:

$$m\lambda = 2d\sin\theta, \quad m = 1, 2, 3\ldots \quad \text{(Bragg's law)}. \qquad (7.1)$$

If only two rows are involved, the transition from constructive to destructive interference as θ changes is gradual. However, if interference from many rows occurs, then the constructive interference peaks become very sharp with mostly destructive interference in between. This sharpening of the peaks as the number of rows increases is very similar to the sharpening of the diffraction peaks from a diffraction grating as the number of slits increases.

7.2 X-Ray Diffraction Techniques

Two types of targets are used in Bragg diffraction experiments: single crystals and powder targets.

7.2.1 Single Crystal

In a single crystal setup, an X-ray detector is mounted as shown in figure 7.2. A mechanical device keeps the detector oriented so that the angle of incidence equals the angle of reflection for the desired crystal plane. Peaks in the X-ray detection rate are sought as the angle θ is varied.

The advantage of this type of apparatus is that diffraction peaks from only the selected crystal plane are observed.

7.2.2 Powder Target

The powder in a powder target is really a conglomeration of many tiny crystals randomly oriented. Thus, for each possible Bragg diffraction angle there are crystals oriented correctly for Bragg diffraction to take place. The detector is usually a photographic plate or an equivalent electronic device as

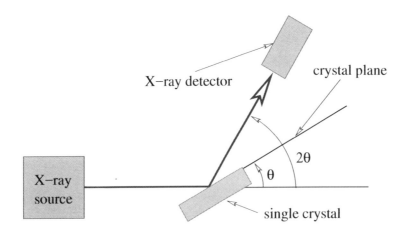

Figure 7.2: Setup for single crystal Bragg diffraction.

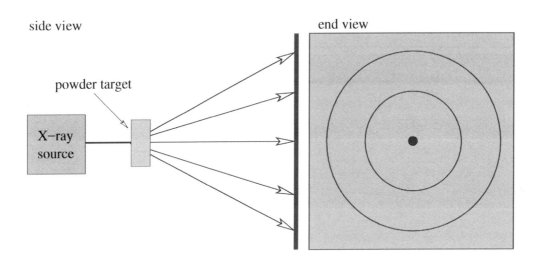

Figure 7.3: Setup for powder target Bragg diffraction.

illustrated in figure 7.3. For each Bragg diffraction angle one sees a ring on the plate concentric with the axis of the incident X-ray beam.

The advantage of this type of system is that no knowledge is needed of the crystal plane orientations. Furthermore, a single large crystal is not required. However, all possible Bragg scattering angles are seen at once, which can lead to confusion in the interpretation of the results.

7.3 Meaning of Quantum Wave Function

Bragg diffraction illustrates the most difficult thing to understand about quantum mechanics, namely that particles can have wave-like properties and waves can have particle-like properties.

The variation of X-ray intensity with angle seen in a Bragg diffraction apparatus is very difficult to explain in any terms other than wave interference. Yet, X-rays are typically detected by a device such as a Geiger counter which produces a pulse of electricity for each X-ray particle, or *photon*, which hits it. Thus, X-rays sometimes act like particles and sometimes like waves.

Light isn't alone in having both particle and wave properties. Davisson and Germer and later G. P. Thomson (son of J. J. Thomson, the discoverer of the electron) showed that electrons also can act like waves. They did this by demonstrating that electrons undergo Bragg diffraction in crystals, much as X-rays do.

Most physicists (including Albert Einstein) have found quantum mechanics to be extremely bizarre, so if you feel the same way, you are in good company! However, there is a useful interpretation of quantum mechanics which at least allows us to get on with using it to solve problems, even though it may not satisfy our intuitive reservations about the theory.

The displacement of the matter wave associated with a particle is usually called the wave function, ψ. It is not at all clear what ψ is a displacement *of*, but its use is straightforward. The absolute square of the wave function, $|\psi(x,t)|^2$, is proportional to the *probability* of finding the associated particle at position x and time t. The *absolute* square is taken because under many circumstances the wave function is actually *complex*, i. e., it has both real and imaginary parts. The reasons for this will be discussed later.

Due to the interpretation of the wave function, quantum mechanics is a probabilistic theory. It does not tell us with certainty what happens to a particular particle. Instead, it tells us the probability for detecting the particle in any given location. If many experiments are done, with one particle per experiment, the numbers of experiments with particles being detected in the various possible locations are in proportion to the quantum mechanical probabilities.

7.4 Sense and Nonsense in Quantum Mechanics

The essential mystery of quantum mechanics becomes clearer when discussed in the conceptually simpler context of two slit interference. If light and electrons can have both particle and wave properties, then one might ask through which of the two slits the particle passed. However, in physics a question simply doesn't make sense if it cannot be answered by experiment.

One can indeed perform an experiment to determine which slit the X-ray photon or electron passes through in the two slit experiment. However, by the very act of making this measurement, the form of the associated wave is altered. In particular, since the absolute square of the wave displacement represents the probability of finding the particle, once the particle has definitely been found passing through one or the other of the slits, the wave function collapses into a very small wave packet located at the observed position of the particle. Thus, the wave displacement becomes zero at the slit it didn't pass through. However, the interference pattern results from the superposition of waves emanating from two slits. If no wave comes from one of the slits (because the wave displacement is zero there), then there can be no interference pattern!

We can now make the inverse argument. If there is an interference pattern, then we know that the wave displacement is non-zero at both slits. From the probability interpretation of the wave displacement, we conclude that we cannot say, even in principle, through which slit the particle passed. It is not just that we don't know the answer to this question; there is simply no experiment which can give us an answer without destroying the interference pattern. In other words, the question "Which slit did the particle pass through?" is a nonsensical question in the case where an interference pattern is actually produced.

The American physicist Richard Feynman noticed that the above behavior can be interpreted as violating the normal laws of probability. These laws say that the probability of an event is the sum of the probabilities of alternate independent ways for that event to occur. For instance, the probability for a particle to reach point A on the detection screen of a two slit setup is just the probability P_1 for the particle to reach point A after going through slit 1, plus the probability P_2 for the particle to reach point A after going through slit 2. Thus, if $P_1 = P_2 = 0.1$, then the probability for the particle to reach point A irrespective of which slit it went through should be $P_{total} = P_1 + P_2 = 0.2$. However, if point A happens to be a point of destructive interference, then we know that $P_{total} = 0$.

Feynman proposed that the above rule stating that alternate independent probabilities add, is simply incorrect. In its place Feynman asserted that *probability amplitudes* add instead, where the probability amplitude in this case is just the wave function associated with the particle. The total probability for a process is obtained by adding the alternate probability amplitudes together and taking the absolute square of the sum.

Feynman's view is a particularly compact expression of the so-called *Copenhagen interpretation* of quantum mechanics which evolved from the ideas of Niels Bohr, Werner Heisenberg, Max Born, and others in the 1920s. It dispenses with the wave-particle duality and other philosophical baggage by saying "Particles are real in that we can observe them, but the only theory we have is about probability amplitudes for particles." This interpretation of quantum mechanics may be weird, but it appears to be self-consistent and in agreement with experiment.

7.5 Mass, Momentum, and Energy

In this section we relate the classical ideas of mass, momentum and energy to what we have done so far. Historically, these connections were first made by Max Planck and Louis de Broglie with help from Albert Einstein. Bragg diffraction of electrons is invoked as an experimental test of the Planck and de Broglie relations.

Technically, we don't need the ideas of mass, momentum, and energy to do physics – the notions of wavenumber, frequency, and group velocity are sufficient to describe and explain all observed phenomena. However, mass, momentum, and energy are so firmly embedded in physics that one couldn't talk to other physicists without an understanding of these quantities!

7.5.1 Planck, Einstein, and de Broglie

Max Planck was the first to develop a theory explaining the energy density of electromagnetic radiation in a box at a fixed temperature. Albert Einstein extended Planck's ideas by postulating that the energy of electromagnetic radiation is quantized into chunks called *photons*. The energy E of a photon is related to the frequency of the electromagnetic radiation by the equation

$$E = hf = \hbar\omega \quad \text{(Planck-Einstein relation)}, \tag{7.2}$$

where f is the rotational frequency of the associated electromagnetic wave and ω is its angular frequency. The constant $h = 6.63 \times 10^{-34}$ kg m^2 s^{-1} is called *Planck's constant*. The related constant $\hbar = h/2\pi = 1.06 \times 10^{-34}$ kg m^2 s^{-1} is also referred to as Planck's constant, but to avoid confusion with the original constant, we will generally refer to it as "h bar".

Notice that a new physical dimension has appeared, namely mass, with the unit *kilogram*, abbreviated "kg". The physical meaning of mass is much like our intuitive understanding of the concept, i. e., as a measure of the resistance of an object to its velocity being changed. The precise scientific meaning will emerge shortly.

Einstein showed that Planck's idea could be used to explain the emission of electrons which occurs when light impinges on the surface of a metal. This emission, which is called the *photoelectric effect*, can only occur when electrons are supplied with a certain minimum energy E_B required to break them loose from the metal. Experiment shows that this emission occurs only when the frequency of the light exceeds a certain minimum value. This value turns out to equal $\omega_{min} = E_B/\hbar$, which suggests that electrons gain energy by absorbing a single photon. If the photon energy, $\hbar\omega$, exceeds E_B, then electrons are emitted, otherwise they are not. It is much more difficult to explain the photoelectric effect from the classical theory of light. The value of E_B, called the binding energy or work function, is different for different metals.

Louis de Broglie proposed that Planck's energy-frequency relationship be extended to all kinds of particles. In addition he hypothesized that the *momentum* $\mathbf{\Pi}$ of the particle and the wave vector $\mathbf{k}$ of the corresponding wave were similarly related:

$$\mathbf{\Pi} = \hbar\mathbf{k} \quad \text{(de Broglie relation)}. \tag{7.3}$$

Note that this can also be written in scalar form in terms of the wavelength as $\Pi = h/\lambda$. (We use $\mathbf{\Pi}$ rather than the more common $\mathbf{p}$ for momentum, because as we shall see, there are two different kinds of momentum, one related to the wavenumber, the other related to the velocity of a particle. In many cases they are equal, but there are certain important situations in which they are not.)

De Broglie's hypothesis was inspired by the fact that wave frequency and wavenumber are components of the same four-vector according to the theory of relativity, and are therefore closely related to each other. Thus, if the energy of a particle is related to the frequency of the corresponding wave, then there ought to be some similar quantity which is correspondingly related to the wavenumber. It turns out that the momentum is the appropriate quantity. The physical meaning of momentum will become clear as we proceed.

We will also find that the rest frequency, μ, of a particle is related to its mass, m:

$$E_{rest} \equiv mc^2 = \hbar\mu. \tag{7.4}$$

The quantity E_{rest} is called the *rest energy* of the particle.

From our perspective, energy, momentum, and rest energy are just scaled versions of frequency, wave vector, and rest frequency, with a scaling factor $\hbar$. We can therefore define a *four-momentum* as a scaled version of the wave four-vector:

$$\underline{\Pi} = \hbar\underline{k}. \tag{7.5}$$

The spacelike component of $\underline{\Pi}$ is just $\mathbf{\Pi}$, while the timelike part is E/c.

Planck, Einstein, and de Broglie had extensive backgrounds in classical mechanics, in which the concepts of energy, momentum, and mass have precise meaning. In this text we do not presuppose such a background. Perhaps the best strategy at this point is to think of these quantities as scaled versions of frequency, wavenumber, and rest frequency, where the scale factor is $\hbar$. The significance of these quantities to classical mechanics will emerge bit by bit.

7.5.2   Wave and Particle Quantities

Let us now recapitulate what we know about relativistic waves, and how this knowledge translates into knowledge about the mass, energy, and momentum of particles. In the following equations, the form on the left is expressed in wave terms, i. e., in terms of frequency, wavenumber, and rest frequency. The form on the right is the identical equation expressed in terms of energy, momentum, and mass. Since the latter variables are just scaled forms of the former, the two forms of each equation are equivalent.

We begin with the dispersion relation for relativistic waves:

$$\omega^2 = k^2 c^2 + \mu^2 \qquad E^2 = \Pi^2 c^2 + m^2 c^4. \tag{7.6}$$

Calculation of the group velocity, $u_g = d\omega/dk$, from the dispersion relation yields

$$u_g = \frac{c^2 k}{\omega} \qquad u_g = \frac{c^2 \Pi}{E}. \tag{7.7}$$

These two sets of equations represent what we know about relativistic waves, and what this knowledge tells us about the relationships between the mass, energy, and momentum of relativistic particles. When in doubt, refer back to these equations, as they work in all cases, including for particles with zero mass!

It is useful to turn equations (7.6) and (7.7) around so as to express the frequency as a function of rest frequency and group velocity,

$$\omega = \frac{\mu}{(1 - u_g^2/c^2)^{1/2}} \qquad E = \frac{mc^2}{(1 - u_g^2/c^2)^{1/2}}, \tag{7.8}$$

and the wavenumber as a similar function of these quantities:

$$k = \frac{\mu u_g/c^2}{(1 - u_g^2/c^2)^{1/2}} \qquad \Pi = \frac{m u_g}{(1 - u_g^2/c^2)^{1/2}}. \tag{7.9}$$

Note that equations (7.8) and (7.9) work only for particles with non-zero mass! For zero mass particles both the numerators and denominators of equations (7.8) and (7.9) are zero, making these equations undefined, and you need to use equations (7.6) and (7.7) with $m = 0$ and $\mu = 0$ instead.

The quantity $\omega - \mu$ indicates how much the frequency exceeds the rest frequency. Notice that if $\omega = \mu$, then from equation (7.6) $k = 0$. Thus, positive values of $\omega_k \equiv \omega - \mu$ indicate $|k| > 0$, which means that the particle is moving according to equation (7.7). Let us call ω_k the *kinetic frequency*:

$$\omega_k = \left[\frac{1}{(1 - u_g^2/c^2)^{1/2}} - 1 \right] \mu \qquad K = \left[\frac{1}{(1 - u_g^2/c^2)^{1/2}} - 1 \right] mc^2. \tag{7.10}$$

We call K the *kinetic energy* for similar reasons. Again, equation (7.10) only works for particles with non-zero mass. For zero mass particles the kinetic energy equals the total energy.

Note that the results of this section are valid only for free particles, i. e., particles to which no force is applied. Force in classical and quantum mechanics is treated in the next chapter.

7.5.3   Non-Relativistic Limits

When the mass is non-zero and the group velocity is much less than the speed of light, it is useful to compute approximate forms of the above equations valid in this limit. Using the approximation $(1 + \epsilon)^x \approx 1 + x\epsilon$, we find that the dispersion relation becomes

$$\omega = \mu + \frac{k^2 c^2}{2\mu} \qquad E = mc^2 + \frac{\Pi^2}{2m}, \tag{7.11}$$

and the group velocity equation takes the approximate form

$$u_g = \frac{c^2 k}{\mu} \qquad u_g = \frac{\Pi}{m}. \tag{7.12}$$

The non-relativistic limits for equations (7.8) and (7.9) become

$$\omega = \mu + \frac{\mu u_g^2}{2c^2} \qquad E = mc^2 + \frac{m u_g^2}{2} \tag{7.13}$$

and

$$k = \mu u_g / c^2 \qquad \Pi = m u_g, \tag{7.14}$$

while the approximate kinetic energy equation is

$$\omega_k = \frac{\mu u_g^2}{2c^2} \qquad K = \frac{m u_g^2}{2}. \tag{7.15}$$

Just a reminder — the equations in this section are not valid for massless particles!

7.5.4   An Experimental Test

How can we test the above predictions against experiment? The key point is to be able to relate the wave aspects to the particle aspects of a quantum mechanical wave-particle. Equation (7.9), or equation (7.14) in the non-relativistic case, relates a particle's wavenumber k to its velocity u_g. Both of these quantities can be measured in a Bragg's law experiment with electrons. In this experiment electrons are fired at a crystal with known atomic dimensions at a known speed, which we identify with the group velocity u_g. The Bragg angle which yields constructive interference can be used to calculate the wavelength of the corresponding electron wave, and hence the wavenumber and momentum. If the momentum is plotted against group velocity in the non-relativistic case, a straight line should be found, the slope of which is the particle's mass. In the fully relativistic case one needs to plot momentum versus $u_g/(1 - u_g^2/c^2)^{1/2}$. Again, a straight line indicates agreement with the theory and the slope of the line is the particle's mass. This particular experiment is difficult to do, but the corresponding theories verify in many other experiments.

7.6 Heisenberg Uncertainty Principle

Classically, we consider the location of a particle to be a knowable piece of information. In quantum mechanics the position of a particle is well known if the wave packet representing it is small in size. However, quantum mechanics imposes a price on accurately knowing the position of a particle in terms of the future predictability of its position. This is because a small wave packet, which corresponds to accurate knowledge of the corresponding particle's position, implies the superposition of plane waves corresponding to a broad distribution of wavenumbers. This translates into a large uncertainty in the wavenumber, and hence the momentum of the particle. In contrast, a broad wave packet corresponds to a narrower distribution of wavenumbers, and correspondingly less uncertainty in the momentum.

Referring back to chapters 1 and 2, recall that both the longitudinal (along the direction of motion) and transverse (normal to the direction of motion) dimensions of a wave packet, Δx_L and Δx_T, can be related to the spread of longitudinal and transverse wavenumbers, Δk_L and Δk_T:

$$\Delta k_L \Delta x_L \approx 1, \tag{7.16}$$

$$\Delta k_T \Delta x_T \approx 1. \tag{7.17}$$

We have omitted numerical constants which are of order unity in these approximate relations so as to show their essential similarity.

The above equations can be interpreted in the following way. Since the absolute square of the wave function represents the probability of finding a particle, Δx_L and Δx_T represent the uncertainty in the particle's position. Similarly, Δk_L and Δk_T represent the uncertainty in the particle's longitudinal and transverse wave vector components. This latter uncertainty leads to uncertainty in the particle's future motion — larger or smaller longitudinal k results respectively in larger or smaller particle speed, while uncertainty in the transverse wavenumber results in uncertainty in the particle's direction of motion. Thus uncertainties in any component of $\mathbf{k}$ result in uncertainties in the corresponding component of the particle's velocity, and hence in its future position.

The equations (7.16) and (7.17) show that uncertainty in the present and future positions of a particle are complimentary. If the present position is accurately known due to the small size of the associated wave packet, then the future position is not very predictable, because the wave packet disperses rapidly. On the other hand, a broad-scale initial wave packet means that the present position is poorly known, but the uncertainty in position, poor as it is, doesn't rapidly increase with time, since the wave packet has a small uncertainty in wave vector and thus disperses slowly. This is a statement of the *Heisenberg uncertainty principle*.

The uncertainty principle also applies between frequency and time:

$$\Delta\omega\Delta t \approx 1. \tag{7.18}$$

This shows up in the beat frequency equation $1/T_{beat} = \Delta f = \Delta\omega/2\pi$. The beat period T_{beat} may be thought of as the size of a "wave packet in time". The beat frequency equation may be rewritten as $\Delta\omega T_{beat} = 2\pi$, which is the same as equation (7.18) if the factor of 2π is ignored and T_{beat} is identified with Δt.

The above forms of the uncertainty principle are not relativistically invariant. A useful invariant form may be obtained by transforming to the coordinate system in which a particle is stationary. In this reference frame the time t becomes the proper time τ associated with the particle. Furthermore, the frequency ω becomes the rest frequency μ. The uncertainty principle thus becomes

$$\Delta\mu\Delta\tau \approx 1 \tag{7.19}$$

in this reference frame. However, since $\Delta\mu$ and $\Delta\tau$ are relativistic invariants, this expression of the uncertainty principle is valid in *any* reference frame.

It is more common to express the uncertainty principle in terms of the mass, momentum, and energy by multiplying equations (7.16) - (7.19) by $\hbar$.

Lumping the momentum equations, we find

$$\Delta\Pi\Delta x \approx \hbar, \tag{7.20}$$

$$\Delta E\Delta t \approx \hbar, \tag{7.21}$$

and

$$\Delta(mc^2)\Delta\tau \approx \hbar. \tag{7.22}$$

Classical mechanics is the realm of quantum mechanics in which the dimensions of the system of interest are much larger than the wavelengths of the waves corresponding to the particles constituting the system. In this case the uncertainties induced by the uncertainty principle are unimportant. This limit is analogous to the geometrical optics limit for light. Thus, we can say that classical mechanics is the geometrical optics limit of quantum mechanics.

7.7 Problems

1. An electron with wavelength $\lambda = 1.2\times10^{-10}$ m undergoes Bragg diffraction from a single crystal with atomic plane spacing of $d = 2\times10^{-10}$ m.

   (a) Calculate the Bragg angles (all of them!) for which constructive interference occurs.

   (b) Calculate the speed of the electron.

2. Suppose that electrons impinge on two slits in a plate, resulting in a two slit diffraction pattern on a screen on the other side of the plate. The probability for an electron to pass through either one of the slits and reach point A on the screen is P, assuming that the other slit is blocked.

   (a) If there are two slits open and A is a point of constructive interference, what is the probability of an electron reaching A? Hint: Remember that amplitudes, not probabilities add.

   (b) If there are two slits open and A is a point of destructive interference, what is the probability of an electron reaching A?

(c) If there are two slits open, what is the probability for an electron to reach point A according to the conventional rule that probabilities add? (This is the result one would expect if, for instance, the particles were machine gun bullets and the slits were, say, 5 cm apart.)

(d) If the slit separation is very much greater than the electron wavelength, how does this affect the spacing of regions of constructive and destructive interference? Explain how the results of parts (a) and (b) become approximately consistent with those of part (c) in this case.

3. Compute the (angular) rest frequency of an electron and a neutron. (Look up their masses.)

4. How does the dispersion relation for relativistic waves simplify if the rest frequency (and hence the particle mass) is zero? What is the group velocity in this case?

5. X-rays are photons with frequencies about 2000 times the frequencies of ordinary light photons. From this information and what you know about light, infer the approximate velocity of electrons which have Bragg diffraction properties similar to X-rays. Are the electrons relativistic or non-relativistic?

6. Electrons with velocity $v = 0.6c$ are diffracted with a 0.2 radian half-angle of diffraction when they hit an object. What is the approximate size of the object? Hint: Diffraction of a wave by an object of a certain size is quite similar to diffraction by a hole in a screen of the same size.

7. Work out an approximate formula for the kinetic energy of a particle as a function of mass m and velocity u_g which is valid when $u_g^2 \ll c^2$. Hint: Use the approximation $(1 + \epsilon)^x \approx 1 + x\epsilon$, which is valid for $|\epsilon| \ll 1$. As u_g/c becomes larger, how does this approximate formula deviate from the exact formula?

8. Work out an approximate formula for the momentum of a particle as a function of m and u_g in the case where $u_g^2 \ll c^2$. You may wish to use the approximation mentioned in the previous problem.

9. If a photon is localized to within a distance Δx, what is the uncertainty in the photon energy?

10. If an electron is localized to within a distance Δx, what is the uncertainty in the electron kinetic energy? Hint: As long as $\Delta\Pi \ll \Pi$, $\Delta\Pi^2 \approx 2\Pi\Delta\Pi$. To see why, compute $d\Pi^2/d\Pi$.

11. A grocer dumps some pinto beans onto a scale, estimates their mass as 2 kg, and then dumps them off after 5 s. What is the quantum mechanical uncertainty in this measurement? Assume this occurs in Quantum World where the speed of light is 10 m s^{-1} (speed of a fast buggy) and Planck's constant $\hbar = 1$ kg m^2 s^{-1}.

12. Mary's physics text (mass 0.3 kg) has to be kept on a leash (length 0.5 m) to prevent it from wandering away from her in Quantum World ($\hbar = 1$ kg m^2 s^{-1}).

    (a) If the leash suddenly breaks, what is the maximum speed at which the book is likely to move away from its initial location?

    (b) In order to reduce this speed, should Mary make the new leash shorter or longer than the old one? Explain.

13. A proton (mass $M = 1.7 \times 10^{-27}$ kg) is confined to an atomic nucleus of diameter $D = 2 \times 10^{-15}$ m.

    (a) What is the uncertainty in the proton's momentum?

    (b) Roughly what kinetic energy might you expect the proton to have?

    Planck's constant is $\hbar = 1.06 \times 10^{-34}$ kg m^2 s^{-1}. You may use the non-relativistic equation for the energy.

Chapter 8

Geometrical Optics and Newton's Laws

The question that motivates us to study physics is "What makes things go?" The answers we conceive to this question constitute the subject of *dynamics*. This is in contrast to the question we have primarily addressed so far, namely "How do things go?" The latter question is about kinematics. Extensive preparation in the kinematics of waves and particles in relativistic spacetime is needed to intelligently address dynamics. This preparation is now complete.

In this chapter we outline three different dynamical principles based respectively on pre-Newtonian, Newtonian, and quantum mechanical thinking. We first discuss the Newtonian mechanics of conservative forces in one dimension. Certain ancillary concepts in mechanics such as work and power are introduced at this stage. We then show that Newtonian and quantum mechanics are consistent with each other in the realm in which they overlap, i. e., in the geometrical optics limit of quantum mechanics. For simplicity, this relationship is first developed in one dimension in the non-relativistic limit. Higher dimensions require the introduction of partial derivatives, and the relativistic case will be considered later.

8.1   Fundamental Principles of Dynamics

Roughly speaking, there have been three eras of physics, characterized by three different answers to the question of what makes things go.

8.1.1 Pre-Newtonian Dynamics

Aristotle expounded a view of dynamics which agrees closely with our everyday experience of the world. Objects only move when a force is exerted upon them. As soon as the force goes away, the object stops moving. The act of pushing a box across the floor illustrates this principle — the box certainly doesn't move by itself!

8.1.2 Newtonian Dynamics

In contrast to earthly behavior, the motions of celestial objects seem effortless. No obvious forces act to keep the planets in motion around the sun. In fact, it appears that celestial objects simply coast along at constant velocity unless something acts on them. The Newtonian view of dynamics — objects change their *velocity* rather than their position when a force is exerted on them — is expressed by *Newton's second law*:

$$\mathbf{F} = m\mathbf{a} \quad \text{(Newton's second law)}, \tag{8.1}$$

where $\mathbf{F}$ is the force exerted on a body, m is its mass, and $\mathbf{a}$ is its acceleration. *Newton's first law*, which states that an object remains at rest or in uniform motion unless a force acts on it, is actually a special case of Newton's second law which applies when $\mathbf{F} = 0$.

It is no wonder that the first successes of Newtonian mechanics were in the celestial realm, namely in the predictions of planetary orbits. It took Newton's genius to realize that the same principles which guided the planets also applied to the earthly realm as well. In the Newtonian view, the tendency of objects to stop when we stop pushing on them is simply a consequence of frictional forces opposing the motion. Friction, which is so important on the earth, is negligible for planetary motions, which is why Newtonian dynamics is more obviously valid for celestial bodies.

Note that the principle of relativity is closely related to Newtonian physics and is incompatible with pre-Newtonian views. After all, two reference frames moving relative to each other cannot be equivalent in the pre-Newtonian view, because objects with nothing pushing on them can only come to rest in one of the two reference frames. Newton's second law obeys the principle of relativity because the acceleration of an object is the same when viewed from two different reference frames moving at a constant velocity with respect to each other.

Einstein's relativity is often viewed as a repudiation of Newton, but this is far from the truth — Newtonian physics makes the theory of relativity possible through its invention of the principle of relativity. Compared with the differences between pre-Newtonian and Newtonian dynamics, the changes needed to go from Newtonian to Einsteinian physics constitute minor tinkering.

8.1.3 Quantum Dynamics

In quantum mechanics, particles are represented by matter waves, with the absolute square of the wave displacement yielding the probability of finding the particle. The behavior of particles thus follows from the reflection, refraction, diffraction, and interference of the associated waves. The connection with Newtonian dynamics comes from tracing the trajectories of matter wave packets. Changes in the speed and direction of motion of these packets correspond to the accelerations of classical mechanics. When wavelengths are small compared to the natural length scale of the problem at hand, the wave packets can be made small, thus pinpointing the position of the associated particle, without generating excessive uncertainty in the particle's momentum. This is the geometrical optics limit of quantum mechanics.

8.2 Potential Energy

We now address Newtonian mechanics in the case where the force on a particle is *conservative*. A conservative force is one that can be derived from a so-called *potential energy U*. We assume that the potential energy of the particle depends only on its position. The force is obtained from the potential energy by the equation

$$F = -\frac{dU}{dx}. \tag{8.2}$$

Using this equation we write Newton's second law as

$$-\frac{dU}{dx} = ma. \tag{8.3}$$

We then notice that the acceleration can be written in terms of the x derivative along the particle's trajectory of $v^2/2$:

$$a = \frac{dv}{dt} = \frac{dv}{dx}\frac{dx}{dt} = \frac{dv}{dx}v = \frac{1}{2}\frac{dv^2}{dx}. \tag{8.4}$$

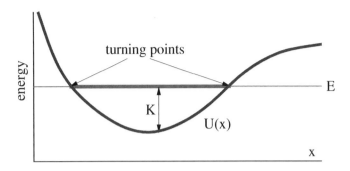

Figure 8.1: Example of spatially variable potential energy $U(x)$ for a particle with fixed total energy E. The kinetic energy $K = E - U$ is zero where the E and U lines cross. These points are called turning points. The thick part of the horizontal line indicates the allowed range for the particle with the given energy.

The last step in the above derivation can be verified by applying the product rule: $dv^2/dt = d(vv)/dt = v(dv/dt) + (dv/dt)v = 2v(dv/dt)$. Putting equations (8.3) and (8.4) together, we find that $d(mv^2/2 + U)/dt = 0$, which implies that $mv^2/2 + U$ is constant. We call this constant the *total energy E* and the quantity $K = mv^2/2$ the *kinetic energy*. We thus have the principle of conservation of energy for conservative forces:

$$E = K + U = \text{constant}. \tag{8.5}$$

Recall that in quantum mechanics the momentum is related to the group velocity u_g by

$$\Pi = mu_g \quad (\text{momentum}) \tag{8.6}$$

in the nonrelativistic case. Equating the group velocity to v and eliminating it in the kinetic energy results in an alternate expression for this quantity:

$$K \equiv \frac{1}{2}mu_g^2 = \frac{\Pi^2}{2m} \quad (\text{kinetic energy}). \tag{8.7}$$

Since the total energy E is constant or *conserved*, increases in the potential energy coincide with decreases in the kinetic energy and vice versa, as is illustrated in figure 8.1. In classical mechanics the kinetic energy cannot be negative, since it is the product of half the mass and the square of the velocity, both of which are positive. Thus, a particle with total energy E and potential energy U is forbidden to venture into regions in which the kinetic energy $K = E - U$ is less than zero.

The points at which the kinetic energy is zero are called *turning points*. This is because a particle decreases in speed as it approaches a turning point, stops there for an instant, and reverses direction. Note also that a particle with a given total energy always has the same speed at some point x regardless of whether it approaches this point from the left or the right:

$$\text{speed} = |u_g| = |\pm [2(E - U)/m]^{1/2}|. \tag{8.8}$$

8.2.1 Gravity as a Conservative Force

An example of a conservative force is gravity. An object of mass m near the surface of the earth has the gravitational potential energy

$$U = mgz \quad \text{(gravity near earth's surface)} \tag{8.9}$$

where z is the height of the object above some reference point such as the earth's surface and $g = 9.8$ m s^{-2} is the local value of the *gravitational field* near the surface. Notice that the gravitational potential energy increases upward. The speed of the object in this case is $|u_g| = [2(E - mgz)/m]^{1/2}$. If $|u_g|$ is known to equal the constant value u_0 at elevation $z = 0$, then equations (8.8) and (8.9) tell us that $u_0 = (2E/m)^{1/2}$ and $|u_g| = (u_0^2 - 2gz)^{1/2}$.

There are certain types of questions which energy conservation cannot directly answer. For instance, if an object is released at elevation h with zero velocity at $t = 0$, at what time will it reach $z = 0$ under the influence of gravity? In such cases it is often easiest to return to Newton's second law. Since the force on the object is $F = -dU/dz = -mg$ in this case, we find that the acceleration is $a = F/m = -mg/m = -g$. However, $a = du/dt = d^2z/dt^2$, so

$$u = -gt + C_1 \qquad z = -gt^2/2 + C_1 t + C_2 \quad \text{(constant gravity)}, \tag{8.10}$$

where C_1 and C_2 are constants to be determined by the initial conditions. These results can be verified by differentiating to see if the original acceleration is recovered. Since $u = 0$ and $z = h$ at $t = 0$, we have $C_1 = 0$ and $C_2 = h$. With these results it is easy to show that the object reaches $z = 0$ when $t = (2h/g)^{1/2}$.

8.3 Work and Power

When a force is exerted on an object, energy is transferred to the object. The amount of energy transferred is called the *work* done on the object. However, energy is only transferred if the object moves. The work W done is

$$W = F\Delta x \tag{8.11}$$

where the distance moved by the object is Δx and the force exerted on it is F. Notice that work can either be positive or negative. The work is positive if the object being acted upon moves in the same direction as the force, with negative work occurring if the object moves opposite to the force.

Equation (8.11) assumes that the force remains constant over the full displacement Δx. If it is not, then it is necessary to break up the displacement into a number of smaller displacements, over each of which the force can be assumed to be constant. The total work is then the sum of the works associated with each small displacement.

If more than one force acts on an object, the works due to the different forces each add or subtract energy, depending on whether they are positive or negative. The total work is the sum of these individual works.

There are two special cases in which the work done on an object is related to other quantities. If F is the total force acting on the object, then $W = F\Delta x = ma\Delta x$ by Newton's second law. However, $a = dv/dt$ where v is the velocity of the object, and $\Delta x = (\Delta x/\Delta t)\Delta t \approx v\Delta t$, where Δt is the time required by the object to move through distance Δx. The approximation becomes exact when Δx and Δt become very small. Putting all of this together results in

$$W_{total} = m\frac{dv}{dt}v\Delta t = \frac{d}{dt}\left(\frac{mv^2}{2}\right)\Delta t = \Delta K \quad \text{(total work)}, \tag{8.12}$$

where K is the kinetic energy of the object. Thus, when F is the only force, $W = W_{total}$ is the total work on the object, and this equals the change in kinetic energy of the object. This is called the *work-energy theorem*, and it demonstrates that work really is a transfer of energy to an object.

The other special case occurs when the force is conservative, but is not necessarily the total force acting on the object. In this case

$$W_{cons} = -\frac{dU}{dx}\Delta x = -\Delta U \quad \text{(conservative force)}, \tag{8.13}$$

where ΔU is the change in the potential energy of the object associated with the force of interest.

The *power* associated with a force is simply the amount of work done by the force divided by the time interval Δt over which it is done. It is therefore the energy per unit time transferred to the object by the force of interest. From equation (8.11) we see that the power is

$$P = \frac{F \Delta x}{\Delta t} = Fv \quad \text{(power)}, \tag{8.14}$$

where v is the velocity at which the object is moving. The *total power* is just the sum of the powers associated with each force. It equals the time rate of change of kinetic energy of the object:

$$P_{total} = \frac{W_{total}}{\Delta t} = \frac{dK}{dt} \quad \text{(total power)}. \tag{8.15}$$

8.4 Mechanics and Geometrical Optics

Louis de Broglie[1] made an analogy between matter waves and light waves, pointing out that wave packets of light change their velocity as the result of spatial variations in the index of refraction of the medium in which they are travelling. This behavior comes about because the dispersion relation for light traveling through a medium with index of refraction n is $\omega = kc/n$, so that the group velocity, $u_g = d\omega/dk = c/n$. Thus, when n increases, u_g decreases, and vice versa.[2]

In this section we pursue de Broglie's analogy to see if we can come up with a theory of matter waves which gives the same results as classical mechanics in the geometrical optics limit of these waves. The dispersion relation for free matter waves is $\omega = (k^2 c^2 + \mu^2)^{1/2}$. In the non-relativistic limit $k^2 c^2 \ll \mu^2$. As done previously, we use $(1 + \epsilon)^n \approx 1 + n\epsilon$ for small ϵ. In the non-relativistic limit, the dispersion relation for free waves thus becomes

$$\omega = \mu(1 + k^2 c^2/\mu^2)^{1/2} \approx \mu + k^2 c^2/(2\mu). \tag{8.16}$$

---

[1] See Louis de Broglie's 1929 Nobel Prize address, reproduced in Boorse, H. A., and L. Motz, 1966: *The World of the Atom*, Basic Books.

[2] This group velocity calculation ignores the possible dependence of index of refraction on wavenumber. If n is a function of k, the calculation is more complicated, but the principle is the same.

The above equation can be transformed into the total energy equation for a free, non-relativistic particle, $E = mc^2 + K$, where mc^2 is the rest energy and K is the kinetic energy, by multiplying by $\hbar$. We convert the free particle energy equation into the equation for a particle subject to a conservative force by adding the potential energy U the right side. The analogous change to equation (8.16) is to add $S = U/\hbar$ to the right side, resulting in a modified dispersion relation:

$$\omega = S(x) + k^2 c^2/(2\mu). \tag{8.17}$$

(Since the rest energy is just a constant, we have absorbed it into S.) This gives us the dispersion relation for one-dimensional matter waves subject to a spatially varying potential energy. The quantity S, which we see is just a scaled potential energy, plays a role for matter waves which is analogous to the role played by a spatially variable index of refraction for light waves.

Let us now imagine that all parts of the wave governed by this dispersion relation oscillate in phase. The only way this can happen is if ω is constant, i. e., it takes on the same value in all parts of the wave.

If ω is constant, the only way S can vary with x in equation (8.17) is if the wavenumber varies in a compensating way. Thus, constant frequency and spatially varying S together imply that $k = k(x)$. Solving equation (8.17) for k yields

$$k(x) = \pm \left[\frac{2\mu[\omega - S(x)]}{c^2} \right]^{1/2}. \tag{8.18}$$

Since ω is constant, the wavenumber becomes smaller and the wavelength larger as the wave moves into a region of increased S.

In the geometrical optics limit, we assume that S doesn't change much over one wavelength so that the wave remains reasonably sinusoidal in shape with approximately constant wavenumber over a few wavelengths. However, over distances of many wavelengths the wavenumber and amplitude of the wave are allowed to vary considerably.

The group velocity calculated from the dispersion relation given by equation (8.17) is

$$u_g = \frac{d\omega}{dk} = \frac{kc^2}{\mu} = \pm \left(\frac{2c^2(\omega - S)}{\mu} \right)^{1/2} \tag{8.19}$$

where k is eliminated in the last step with the help of equation (8.18). The resulting equation tells us how the group velocity varies as a matter wave traverses a region of slowly varying S. Thus, as S increases, u_g decreases and vice versa.

We can now calculate the acceleration of a wave packet resulting from the spatial variation in S. We assume that $x(t)$ represents the position of the wave packet, so that $u_g = dx/dt$. Using the chain rule $du_g/dt = (du_g/dx)(dx/dt) = (du_g/dx)u_g$, we find

$$a = \frac{du_g}{dt} = \frac{du_g}{dx}u_g = \frac{du_g^2/2}{dx} = -\frac{c^2}{\mu}\frac{dS}{dx} = -\frac{\hbar}{m}\frac{dS}{dx}. \quad (8.20)$$

The group velocity is eliminated in favor of S by squaring equation (8.19) and substituting the result into equation (8.20).

Recalling that $U = \hbar S$, equation (8.20) becomes

$$a = -\frac{1}{m}\frac{dU}{dx} = \frac{F}{m}, \quad (8.21)$$

which is just Newton's second law! Thus, the geometrical optics approach to particle motion is completely equivalent to the classical mechanics of a particle moving under the influence of a conservative force, at least in one dimension. We therefore have two ways of solving for the motion of a particle subject to a potential energy $U(x)$. We can apply the principles of classical mechanics to get the force and the acceleration of the particle, from which we can derive the motion. Alternatively, we can apply the principles of geometrical optics to compute the spatially variable velocity of the wave packet using equation (8.19). The results are completely equivalent, though the methods are conceptually very different.

8.5 Math Tutorial – Partial Derivatives

In order to understand the generalization of Newtonian mechanics to two and three dimensions, we first need to understand a new type of derivative called the *partial derivative*. The partial derivative is used in functions of more than one variable. It is just like an ordinary derivative, except that when taking the derivative of the function with respect to one of the variables, the other variables are held constant. As an example, let us consider the function

$$f(x,y) = Ax^4 + Bx^2y^2 + Cy^4 \quad (8.22)$$

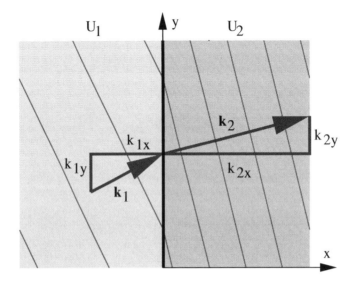

Figure 8.2: Refraction of a matter wave by a discontinuity in potential energy. The component of the wave vector parallel to the discontinuity, k_y, doesn't change, so $k_{1y} = k_{2y}$.

where A, B, and C are constants. The partial derivative of f with respect to x is

$$\frac{\partial f}{\partial x} = 4Ax^3 + 2Bxy^2 \tag{8.23}$$

and the partial derivative with respect to y is

$$\frac{\partial f}{\partial y} = 2Bx^2y + 4Cy^3. \tag{8.24}$$

That's it! Note that a special symbol "∂" is used in place of the normal "d" for the partial derivative. This is sometimes called a "curly d".

8.6 Motion in Two and Three Dimensions

When a matter wave moves through a region of variable potential energy in one dimension, only the wavenumber changes. In two or three dimensions, the wave vector can change in both direction and magnitude. This complicates the calculation of particle movement. However, we already have an example of how to handle this situation, namely, the refraction of light. In that case Snell's law tells us how the direction of the wave vector changes, while the dispersion relation combined with the constancy of the frequency gives us information about the change in the magnitude of the wave vector. For matter waves a similar procedure works, though the details are different, because we seek the consequences of a change in potential energy rather than a change in the index of refraction.

Figure 8.2 illustrates the refraction of matter waves at a discontinuity in the potential energy. Let us suppose that the discontinuity occurs at $x = 0$. If the matter wave to the left of the discontinuity is $\psi_1 = \sin(k_{1x}x + k_{1y}y - \omega_1 t)$ and to the right is $\psi_2 = \sin(k_{2x}x + k_{2y}y - \omega_2 t)$, then the wavefronts of the waves will match across the discontinuity for all time only if $\omega_1 = \omega_2 \equiv \omega$ and $k_{1y} = k_{2y} \equiv k_y$. We are already familiar with the first condition from the one-dimensional problem, so the only new ingredient is the constancy of the y component of the wave vector.

In two dimensions the momentum is a vector: $\mathbf{\Pi} = m\mathbf{u}$ when $|\mathbf{u}| \ll c$, where $\mathbf{u}$ is the particle velocity. Furthermore, the kinetic energy is $K = m|\mathbf{u}|^2/2 = |\mathbf{\Pi}|^2/(2m) = (\Pi_x^2 + \Pi_y^2)/(2m)$. The relationship between kinetic, potential, and total energy is unchanged from the one-dimensional case, so we have

$$E = U + (\Pi_x^2 + \Pi_y^2)/(2m) = \text{constant}. \tag{8.25}$$

The de Broglie relationship tells us that $\mathbf{\Pi} = \hbar\mathbf{k}$, so the constancy of k_y across the discontinuity in U tells us that

$$\Pi_y = \text{constant} \tag{8.26}$$

there.

Let us now approximate a continuously variable $U(x)$ by a series of steps of constant U oriented normal to the x axis. The above analysis can be applied at the jumps or discontinuities in U between steps, as illustrated in figure 8.3, with the result that equations (8.25) and (8.26) are valid across all discontinuities. If we now let the step width go to zero, these equations then become valid for U continuously variable in x.

An example from classical mechanics of a problem of this type is a ball rolling down an inclined ramp with an initial velocity component across the ramp, as illustrated in figure 8.4. The potential energy decreases in the down ramp direction, resulting in a force down the ramp. This accelerates the ball

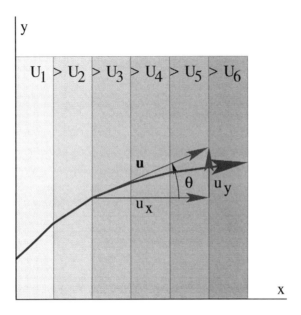

Figure 8.3: Trajectory of a wave packet through a variable potential energy, $U(x)$, which decreases to the right.

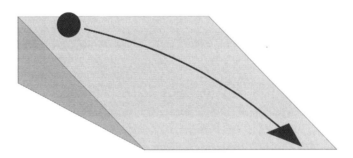

Figure 8.4: Classical mechanics example of the problem illustrated in figure 8.3.

in that direction, but leaves the component of momentum across the ramp unchanged.

Using the procedure which we invoked before, we find the force components associated with $U(x)$ in the x and y directions to be $F_x = -dU/dx$ and $F_y = 0$. This generalizes to

$$\mathbf{F} = -\left(\frac{\partial U}{\partial x}, \frac{\partial U}{\partial y}, \frac{\partial U}{\partial z}\right) \quad \text{(3-D conservative force)} \tag{8.27}$$

in the three-dimensional case where the orientation of constant U surfaces is arbitrary. It is also valid when $U(x, y, z)$ is not limited to a simple ramp form, but takes on a completely arbitrary structure.

The definitions of work and power are slightly different in two and three dimensions. In particular, work is defined as

$$W = \mathbf{F} \cdot \Delta\mathbf{x} \tag{8.28}$$

where $\Delta\mathbf{x}$ is now a vector displacement. The vector character of this expression yields an additional possibility over the one dimensional case, where the work is either positive or negative depending on the direction of $\Delta\mathbf{x}$ relative to $\mathbf{F}$. If the force and the displacement of the object on which the force is acting are perpendicular to each other, the work done by the force is actually zero, even though the force and the displacement both have non-zero magnitudes. The power exhibits a similar change:

$$P = \mathbf{F} \cdot \mathbf{u}. \tag{8.29}$$

Thus the power is zero if an object's velocity is normal to the force being exerted on it.

As in the one-dimensional case, the total work done on a particle equals the change in the particle's kinetic energy. In addition, the work done by a conservative force equals minus the change in the associated potential energy.

Energy conservation by itself is somewhat less useful for solving problems in two and three dimensions than it is in one dimension. This is because knowing the kinetic energy at some point tells us only the magnitude of the velocity, not its direction. If conservation of energy fails to give us the information we need, then we must revert to Newton's second law, as we did in the one-dimensional case. For instance, if an object of mass m has initial velocity $\mathbf{u}_0 = (u_0, 0)$ at location $(x, z) = (0, h)$ and has the gravitational potential energy $U = mgz$, then the force on the object is $\mathbf{F} = (0, -mg)$. The acceleration is therefore $\mathbf{a} = \mathbf{F}/m = (0, -g)$. Since $\mathbf{a} = d\mathbf{u}/dt = d^2\mathbf{x}/dt^2$ where $\mathbf{x} = (x, z)$ is the object's position, we find that

$$\mathbf{u} = (C_1, -gt + C_2) \qquad \mathbf{x} = (C_1 t + C_3, -gt^2/2 + C_2 t + C_4), \qquad (8.30)$$

where C_1, C_2, C_3, and C_4 are constants to be evaluated so that the solution reduces to the initial conditions at $t = 0$. The specified initial conditions tell us that $C_1 = u_0$, $C_2 = 0$, $C_3 = 0$, and $C_4 = h$ in this case. From these results we can infer the position and velocity of the object at any time.

8.7 Kinetic and Total Momentum

If you have previously taken a physics course then you have probably noticed that a rather odd symbol is used for momentum, namely $\mathbf{\Pi}$, rather than the more commonly employed $\mathbf{p}$. The reason for this peculiar usage is that there are actually two kinds of momentum, *kinetic momentum* and *total momentum*, just as there are two kinds of energy, kinetic and total.[3] The symbol $\mathbf{\Pi}$ represents total momentum while $\mathbf{p}$ represents kinetic momentum. Normally we don't need to distinguish between the two quantities, as they are generally equal to each other. However, we will find later in the course that it is crucial to make this distinction in the case of charged particles in a magnetic field. As a general rule, the total momentum is related to a particle's wave vector via the de Broglie relation, $\mathbf{\Pi} = \hbar\mathbf{k}$, while the kinetic momentum is related to a particle's velocity, $\mathbf{p} = m\mathbf{u}/(1 - u^2/c^2)^{1/2}$.

8.8 Problems

1. Suppose the dispersion relation for a matter wave under certain conditions is $\omega = \mu + (k - a)^2 c^2/(2\mu)$ where k is the wavenumber of the wave, $\mu = mc^2/\hbar$, m is the associated particle's mass, a is a constant, c is the speed of light, and $\hbar$ is Planck's constant divided by 2π.

   (a) Use this disperson relation and the Planck and de Broglie relations to determine the relationship between energy E, momentum Π, and mass m.

---

[3]In advanced mechanics the total momentum is called the *canonical momentum* and the kinetic momentum is the ordinary momentum.

Figure 8.5: A wave function in which the wavelength varies with position.

———————————————

    (b) Compute the group velocity of the wave and use this to determine how the group velocity depends on mass and momentum in this case.

2. A matter wave function associated with a particle of definite (constant) total energy E takes the form shown in figure 8.5. Make a sketch showing how the kinetic, potential, and total energies of the particle vary with x.

3. Compute $\partial/\partial x$ and $\partial/\partial y$ of the following functions. Other symbols are constants.

    (a) $f(x,y) = ax^2 + by^3$

    (b) $f(x,y) = ax^2y^2$

    (c) $f(x,y) = (x+a)/(y+b)$

4. Given a potential energy for a particle of mass M of the form $U(x) = Ax^3 - Bx$ where A and B are positive constants:

    (a) Find the force on the particle.

    (b) Find the values of x where the force is zero.

    (c) Sketch $U(x)$ versus x and graphically compare the slope of $U(x)$ to the force computed above. Do the two qualitatively match?

    (d) If the total energy of the particle is zero, where are its turning points?

    (e) What is the particle's speed as a function of position assuming that the total energy E is known?

5. Given a potential energy function $U(x,y) = A(x^2 + y^2)$ where A is a positive constant:

  (a) Sketch lines of constant U in the x-y plane.

  (b) Compute the components of force as a function of x and y and draw sample force vectors in the x-y plane on the same plot used above. Do the force vectors point "uphill" or "downhill"?

6. Do the same as in the previous question for the potential energy function $U(x, y) = Axy$.

7. Suppose that the components of the force vector in the x-y plane are $\mathbf{F} = (2Axy^3, 3Ax^2y^2)$ where A is a constant. See if you can find a potential energy function $U(x, y)$ which gives rise to this force.

8. You are standing on top of a cliff of height H with a rock of mass M.

  (a) If you throw the rock horizontally outward at speed u_0, what will its speed be when it hits the ground below?

  (b) If you throw the rock upward at $45°$ to the horizontal at speed u_0, what will its speed be when it hits the ground?

Hint: Can you use conservation of energy to solve this problem? Ignore air friction.

9. A car of mass 1200 kg initially moving 30 m s^{-1} brakes to a stop.

  (a) What is the net work done on the car due to all the forces acting on it during the indicated period?

  (b) Describe the motion of the car relative to an inertial reference frame initially moving with the car.

  (c) In the above reference frame, what is the net work done on the car during the indicated period?

Is work a relativistically invariant quantity?

10. A soccer player kicks a soccer ball, which is caught by the goal keeper as shown in figure 8.6. At various points forces exerted by gravity, air friction, the foot of the offensive player, and the hands of the goal keeper act on the ball.

  (a) List the forces acting on the soccer ball at each of the points A, B, C, D, and E.

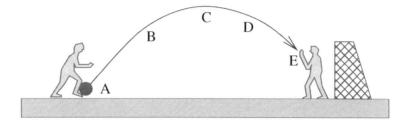

Figure 8.6: The trajectory of a soccer ball.

(b) State whether the instantaneous power being applied to the soccer ball due to each of the forces listed above is positive, negative, or zero at each of the labeled points.

11. A cannon located at $(x, z) = (0, 0)$ shoots a cannon ball upward at an angle of θ from the horizontal at initial speed u_0. Hint: In order to solve this problem you must first obtain the x and z components of acceleration from Newton's second law. Second, you must find the velocity components as a function of time from the components of acceleration. Third, you must find x and z as a function of time from the the components of velocity. Only then should you attempt to answer the questions below.

(a) How long does it take the cannon ball to reach its peak altitude?

(b) How high does the cannon ball go?

(c) At what value of x does the cannon ball hit the ground $(z = 0)$?

(d) Determine what value of θ yields the maximum range.

Chapter 9

Symmetry and Bound States

When quantum mechanics was first invented, the dynamical principles used were the same as those underlying classical mechanics. The initial development of the field thus proceeded largely by imposing quantum laws on classical variables such as position, momentum, and energy. However, as quantum mechanics advanced, it became clear that there were many situations in which no classical analogs existed for new types of quantum mechanical systems, especially those which arose in the study of elementary particles. To understand these systems it was necessary to seek guidance from novel sources. One of the most important of these sources was the idea of symmetry, and in particular the relationship between symmetry and conserved variables. This type of relationship was first developed in the early 20th century by the German mathematician Emmy Nöther in the context of classical mechanics. However, her idea is easier to express and use in quantum mechanics than it is in classical mechanics. Emmy Nöther showed that there is a relationship between the symmetries of a system and conserved dynamical variables. This idea is naturally called *Nöther's theorem*.

In classical mechanics a particle is bound or confined to a particular region if its total energy exceeds the potential energy only in this region. In quantum mechanics, matter waves can also be confined for the same reason, though the confinement is often less perfect than in the classical case. In this chapter we examine the consequences of wave confinement. We first look at the so-called "particle in a box" in one spatial dimension. We find that confined particles can take on only discrete energy values. When confinement isn't perfect we see how a quantum mechanical particle can leak through a potential energy barrier which is classically impenetrable. Movement of a particle on a circular ring leads us to another form of confinement and the introduction of angular momentum. This brings us finally to a discussion of the intrinsic or spin angular momentum of elementary particles.

9.1 Math Tutorial — Complex Waves

Until now we have represented quantum mechanical plane waves by sine and cosine functions, just as with other types of waves. However, plane matter waves cannot be truly represented by sines and cosines. We need instead mathematical functions in which the wave displacement is complex rather than real. This requires the introduction of a bit of new mathematics, which we tackle first. Using our new mathematical tool, we are then able to explore two crucially important ideas in quantum mechanics; (1) the relationship between symmetry and conservation laws, and (2) the dynamics of spatially confined waves.

A *complex number* z is the sum of a real number and an imaginary number. An imaginary number is just a real number multiplied by $i \equiv (-1)^{1/2}$. Thus, we can write $z = a + ib$ for any complex z, where a and b are real. The quantities a and b are the *real* and *imaginary* parts of z, sometimes written $\text{Re}(z)$ and $\text{Im}(z)$.

Quantum mechanics requires wave functions to be complex, i. e., to possess real and imaginary parts. Plane waves in quantum mechanics actually take the form $\psi = \exp[i(kx - \omega t)]$ rather than, say, $\cos(kx - \omega t)$. The reason for this is the need to distinguish between waves with positive and negative frequencies. If we replace k and ω with $-k$ and $-\omega$ in the cosine form, we get $\cos(-kx + \omega t) = \cos[-(kx - \omega t)] = \cos(kx - \omega t)$. In other words, changing the sign of k and ω results in no change in a wave expressed as a cosine function. The two quantum mechanical states, one with wavenumber and frequency k and ω and the other with $-k$ and $-\omega$, yield indistinguishable wave functions and therefore would represent physically indistinguishable states. The cosine form is thus insufficiently flexible to represent quantum mechanical waves. On the other hand, if we replace k and ω with their negatives in the complex exponential form of a plane wave we get $\psi = \exp[-i(kx - \omega t)]$, which is different from $\exp[i(kx - \omega t)]$. These two wave functions are distinguishable and thus correspond to distinct physical states.

It is not immediately obvious that a complex exponential function provides the oscillatory behavior needed to represent a plane wave. However,

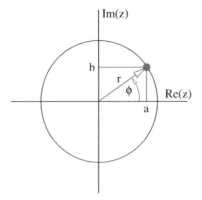

Figure 9.1: Graphical representation of a complex number z as a point in the complex plane. The horizontal and vertical Cartesian components give the real and imaginary parts of z respectively.

the complex exponential can be expressed in terms of sines and cosines using Euler's equation:

$$\exp(i\phi) = \cos(\phi) + i\sin(\phi) \quad \text{(Euler's equation)}. \qquad (9.1)$$

If we define $r = (a^2 + b^2)^{1/2}$ and $\phi = \tan^{-1}(b/a)$, then an alternate way of expressing a complex number is $z = r\exp(i\phi)$, which by Euler's equation equals $r\cos(\phi) + ir\sin(\phi)$. Comparison shows that $a = r\cos(\phi)$ and $b = r\sin(\phi)$. Thus, a complex number can be thought of as a point in the a-b plane with Cartesian coordinates a and b and polar coordinates r and ϕ. The a-b plane is called the *complex plane*.

We now see how the complex wave function represents an oscillation. If $\psi = \exp[i(kx - \omega t)]$, the complex function $\psi(x,t)$ moves round and round the unit circle in the complex plane as x and t change, as illustrated in figure 9.1. This contrasts with the back and forth oscillation along the horizontal axis of the complex plane represented by $\cos(kx - \omega t)$.

We will not present a formal proof of Euler's equation — you will eventually see it in your calculus course. However, it may be helpful to note that the ϕ derivatives of $\exp(i\phi)$ and $\cos(\phi) + i\sin(\phi)$ have the same behavior:

$$\frac{d}{d\phi}\exp(i\phi) = i\exp(i\phi); \qquad (9.2)$$

$$\frac{d}{d\phi}[\cos(\phi) + i\sin(\phi)] = -\sin(\phi) + i\cos(\phi)$$

$$= i[\cos(\phi) + i\sin(\phi)]. \qquad (9.3)$$

(In the second of these equations we have replaced the minus sign in front of the sine function by i^2 and then extracted a common factor of i.) The ϕ derivative of both of these functions thus yields the function back again times i. This is a strong hint that $\exp(i\phi)$ and $\cos(\phi) + i\sin(\phi)$ are different ways of representing the same function.

We indicate the *complex conjugate* of a complex number z by a superscripted asterisk, i. e., z^*. It is obtained by replacing i by $-i$. Thus, $(a + ib)^* = a - ib$. The *absolute square* of a complex number is the number times its complex conjugate:

$$|z|^2 = |a + ib|^2 \equiv (a + ib)(a - ib) = a^2 + b^2 = r^2. \qquad (9.4)$$

Notice that the absolute square of a complex exponential function is one:

$$|\exp(i\phi)|^2 = \exp(i\phi)\exp(-i\phi) = \exp(i\phi - i\phi) = \exp(0) = 1. \qquad (9.5)$$

In quantum mechanics the absolute square of the wave function at any point expresses the relative probability of finding the associated particle at that point. Thus, the probability of finding a particle represented by a plane wave is uniform in space. Contrast this with the relative probability associated with a sine wave: $|\sin(kx - \omega t)|^2 = \sin^2(kx - \omega t)$. This varies from zero to one, depending on the phase of the wave. The "waviness" in a complex exponential plane wave resides in the phase rather than in the magnitude of the wave function.

One more piece of mathematics is needed. The complex conjugate of Euler's equation is

$$\exp(-i\phi) = \cos(\phi) - i\sin(\phi). \qquad (9.6)$$

Taking the sum and the difference of this with the original Euler's equation results in the expression of the sine and cosine in terms of complex exponentials:

$$\cos(\phi) = \frac{\exp(i\phi) + \exp(-i\phi)}{2} \qquad \sin(\phi) = \frac{\exp(i\phi) - \exp(-i\phi)}{2i}. \qquad (9.7)$$

We aren't used to having complex numbers show up in physical theories and it is hard to imagine how we would measure such a number. However, everything observable comes from taking the absolute square of a wave function, so we deal only with real numbers in experiments.

9.2 Symmetry and Quantum Mechanics

The idea of symmetry plays a huge role in physics. We have already used symmetry arguments in the theory of relativity — applying the principle of relativity to obtain the dispersion relation for relativistic matter waves is just such an argument. In this section we begin to explore how symmetry can be used to increase our understanding of quantum mechanics.

9.2.1 Free Particle

For our first example we take the case of a free particle in quantum mechanics, i. e., a particle subject to no force. The wave function for a free particle of definite momentum Π and energy E is given by

$$\psi = \exp[i(kx - \omega t)] = \exp[i(\Pi x - Et)/\hbar] \quad \text{(free particle)}. \qquad (9.8)$$

For this wave function $|\psi|^2 = 1$ everywhere, so the probability of finding the particle anywhere in space and time is uniform. This contrasts with the probability distribution which arises if we assume a free particle to have the wave function $\psi = \cos[(\Pi x - Et)/\hbar]$. In this case $|\psi|^2 = \cos^2[(\Pi x - Et)/\hbar]$, which varies with position and time, and is inconsistent with a uniform probability distribution.

9.2.2 Symmetry and Definiteness

Quantum mechanics is a probabilistic theory, in the sense that the predictions it makes tell us, for instance, the probability of finding a particle somewhere in space. If we know nothing about a particle's previous history, and if there are no physical constraints that would make it more likely for a particle to be at one point along the x axis than any another, then the probability distribution must be $P(x) = constant$.

This is an example of a *symmetry* argument. Expressed more formally, it states that if the above conditions apply, then the probability distribution ought to be subject to the condition $P(x + D) = P(x)$ for any constant value of D. The only possible $P(x)$ in this case is $P = constant$. In the language of physics, if there is nothing that gives the particle a higher probability of being at one point rather than another, then the probability is independent of position and the system is *invariant under displacement* in the x direction.

The above argument doesn't suffice for quantum mechanics, since as we have learned, the fundamental quantity describing a particle is not the probability distribution, but the wave function $\psi(x)$. Thus, the wave function rather than the probability distribution ought to be the quantity which is invariant under displacement, i. e., $\psi(x + D) = \psi(x)$.

This condition turns out to be too restrictive, because it implies that $\psi(x) = constant$, whereas we know that a one-dimensional plane wave, which describes a particle with a uniform probability of being found anywhere along the x axis, has the form $\psi(x) = \exp(ikx)$. (For simplicity we temporarily ignore the time dependence.) If we make the substitution $x \rightarrow x + D$ in a plane wave, we get $\exp[ik(x + D)] = \exp(ikx)\exp(ikD)$. The wave function is thus technically not invariant under displacement, in that the displaced wave function is multiplied by the factor $\exp(ikD)$. However, the probability distribution of the displaced wave function still equals one everywhere, so there is no change in what we observe. Thus, in determining invariance under displacement, we are allowed to ignore changes in the wave function which consist only of multiplying it by a complex constant with an absolute value of one. Such a multiplicative constant is called a *phase factor*.

It is easy to convince oneself by trial and error or by more sophisticated means that the only form of wave function $\psi(x)$ which satisfies the condition $\psi(x+D) = \psi(x) \times$ (phase factor) is $\psi(x) = A\exp(ikx)$ where A is a (possibly complex) constant. This is just in the form of a complex exponential plane wave with wavenumber k. Thus, not only is the complex exponential wave function invariant under displacements in the manner defined above, it is the *only* wave function which is invariant to displacements. Furthermore, the phase factor which appears for a displacement D of such a plane wave takes the form $\exp(iC) = \exp(ikD)$, where k is the wavenumber of the plane wave.

As an experiment, let us see if a wave packet is invariant under displacement. Let's define a wave packet consisting of two plane waves:

$$\psi(x) = \exp(ik_1 x) + \exp(ik_2 x). \tag{9.9}$$

Making the substitution $x \rightarrow x + D$ in this case results in

$$\begin{aligned} \psi(x + D) &= \exp[ik_1(x + D)] + \exp[ik_2(x + D)] \\ &= \exp(ik_1 x)\exp(ik_1 D) + \exp(ik_2 x)\exp(ik_2 D) \\ &\neq [\exp(ik_1 x) + \exp(ik_2 x)] \times \text{(phase factor)}. \end{aligned} \tag{9.10}$$

The impossibility of writing $\psi(x + D) = \psi(x) \times$ (phase factor) lends plausibility to the assertion that a single complex exponential is the only possible form of the wave function that is invariant under displacement.

Notice that the wave packet does not have definite wavenumber, and hence, momentum. In particular, the wave packet is a sum of complex exponentials with wavenumbers k_1 and k_2, which means that the associated particle can have either momentum $\Pi_1 = \hbar k_1$ or $\Pi_2 = \hbar k_2$. This makes sense from the point of view of the uncertainty principle – for a single plane wave the uncertainty in position is complete and the uncertainty in momentum is zero. For a wave packet the uncertainty in position is reduced and the uncertainty in the momentum is non-zero. As we have seen, this idea can be carried further: A definite value of momentum must be associated with a completely indefinite probability distribution in position, i. e., with $P = constant$. This corresponds to a wave function which has the form of a complex exponential plane wave. However, such a plane wave is invariant under displacement D, except for the multiplicative phase factor $\exp(ikD)$, which has no physical consequences since it disappears when the probability distribution is obtained. Thus, we see that invariance under displacement of the wave function and a definite value of the momentum are linked, in that each implies the other:

$$\text{invariance under displacement} \iff \text{definite momentum} \qquad (9.11)$$

The idea of potential energy was introduced in the previous chapter. In particular, we found that if the total energy is constant, then the momentum cannot be constant in the presence of spatially varying potential energy. This means that the wavenumber, and hence the wavelength of the oscillations in the wave function also vary with position. The spatial inhomogeneity of the potential energy gives rise to spatial inhomogeneity in the wave function, and hence an indefinite momentum.

The above argument can be extended to other variables besides momentum. In particular since the time dependence of a complex exponential plane wave is $\exp(-i\omega t) = \exp(-iEt/\hbar)$, where E is the total energy, we have by analogy with the above argument that

$$\text{invariance under time shift} \iff \text{definite energy.} \qquad (9.12)$$

Thus, invariance of the wave function under a displacement in time implies a definite value of the energy of the associated particle.

In the previous chapter we assumed that the frequency (and hence the energy) was definite and constant for a particle passing through a region of variable potential energy. We now see that this assumption is justified only if the potential energy doesn't change with time. This is because a time-varying potential energy eliminates the possibility of invariance under time shift.

9.2.3 Invariance

We have seen a few examples of invariance in quantum mechanics. It is now time to define this concept more precisely. A quantum mechanical wave function is said to be invariant under some transformation if the transformed wave function is observationally indistinguishable from the original.

In the above examples, the transformation is accomplished by replacing x by $x + D$ in the case of displacement in space and similarly by replacing t by $t + T$ for displacement in time. However, the idea of a transformation is much more general; other examples will be discussed as they arise.

The idea of "observationally indistinguishable" can be tricky. For example, if some transformation results in a new wave function which is the old wave function times a constant phase factor, then the new wave function is observationally indistinguishable from the old one. This is because physical measurements capture phase differences between different parts of wave functions (think of how interferometers work), but not absolute phases. The constant phase factor disappears in this difference calculation. However, if the multiplicative phase factor created by some transformation is a function of position, then the phase difference between different parts of a wave function changes as a result of the transformation. The wave function is not invariant under this transformation.

9.2.4 Compatible Variables

We already know that definite values of certain pairs of variables cannot be obtained simultaneously in quantum mechanics. For instance, the indefinite-ness of position and momentum are related by the uncertainty principle — a definite value of position implies an indefinite value of the momentum and vice versa. If definite values of two variables can be simultaneously obtained, then we call these variables *compatible*. If not, the variables are *incompatible*.

If the wave function of a particle is invariant under the displacements associated with both variables, then the variables are compatible. For instance, the complex exponential plane wave associated with a free particle

Heisenberg's Matrix mechanics

Noether's Theorem?

is invariant under displacements in both space and time. Since momentum is associated with space displacements and energy with time displacements, the momentum and energy are compatible variables for a free particle.

9.2.5 Compatibility and Conservation

Variables which are compatible with the energy have a special status. The wave function which corresponds to a definite value of such a variable is invariant to displacements in time. In other words, the wave function doesn't change under this displacement except for a trivial phase factor. Thus, if the wave function is also invariant to some other transformation at a particular time, it is invariant to that transformation for all time. The variable associated with that transformation therefore retains its definite value for all time — i. e., it is *conserved*.

For example, the plane wave implies a definite value of energy, and is thus invariant under time displacements. At time $t = 0$, it is also invariant under x displacements, which corresponds to the fact that it represents a particle with a known value of momentum. However, since momentum and energy are compatible for a free particle, the wave function will represent the *same* value of momentum at all other times. In other words, if the momentum is definite at $t = 0$, it will be definite at all later times, and furthermore will have the same value. This is how the conservation of momentum (and by extension, the conservation of any other variable compatible with energy) is expressed in quantum mechanics.

9.2.6 New Symmetries and Variables

In modern quantum physics, the discovery of new symmetries leads to new dynamical variables. In the problems we show how that comes about for the symmetries of *parity* $(x \rightarrow -x)$, *time reversal* $t \rightarrow -t)$, and *charge conjugation* (the interchange of particles with antiparticles). One of the key examples of this was the development of the quark theory of matter, which came from the observation that the interchange of certain groups of elementary particles left the universe approximately unchanged, meaning that the universe was (approximately) symmetric under these interchanges.

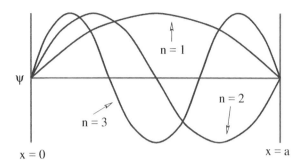

Figure 9.2: First three modes for wave function of a particle in a box.

9.3 Confined Matter Waves

Confinement of a wave to a limited spatial region results in rather peculiar behavior — the wave can only fit comfortably into the confined region if the wave frequency, and hence the associated particle energy, takes on a limited set of possible values. This is the origin of the famous quantization of energy, from which the "quantum" in quantum mechanics comes. We will explore two types of confinement, position confinement due to a potential energy well, and rotational confinement due to the fact that rotation of an object through 2π radians returns the object to its original orientation.

9.3.1 Particle in a Box

We now imagine how a particle confined to a region $0 \leq x \leq a$ on the x axis must behave. As with the displacement of a guitar string, the wave function must be zero at $x = 0$ and a, i. e., at the ends of the guitar string. A single complex exponential plane wave cannot satisfy this condition, since $|\exp[i(kx - \omega t)]|^2 = 1$ everywhere. However, a superposition (with a minus sign) of leftward and rightward traveling waves creates a *standing wave*, in which the the wave function separates into a function of space alone times a function of time alone.

$$\psi = \exp[i(kx - \omega t)] - \exp[i(-kx - \omega t)] = 2i \exp(-i\omega t) \sin(kx). \quad (9.13)$$

Notice that the time dependence is still a complex exponential, which means that $|\psi|^2$ is independent of time. This insures that the probability of finding the particle *somewhere* in the box remains constant with time. It also means that the wave packet corresponds to a definite energy $E = \hbar\omega$.

Because we took a difference rather than a sum of plane waves, the condition $\psi = 0$ is already satisfied at $x = 0$. To satisfy it at $x = a$, we must have $ka = n\pi$, where $n = 1, 2, 3, \ldots$. Thus, the absolute value of the wavenumber must take on the discrete values

$$k_n = \frac{n\pi}{a}, \qquad n = 1, 2, 3, \ldots. \qquad (9.14)$$

(The wavenumbers of the two plane waves equal plus or minus this absolute value respectively.) This implies that the absolute value of the particle momentum is $\Pi_n = \hbar k_n = n\pi\hbar/a$, which in turn means that the energy of the particle must be

$$E_n = (\Pi_n^2 c^2 + m^2 c^4)^{1/2} = (n^2 \pi^2 \hbar^2 c^2/a^2 + m^2 c^4)^{1/2}, \qquad (9.15)$$

where m is the particle mass. In the non-relativistic limit this becomes

$$E_n = \frac{\Pi_n^2}{2m} = \frac{n^2 \pi^2 \hbar^2}{2ma^2} \quad \text{(non-relativistic)} \qquad (9.16)$$

where we have dropped the rest energy mc^2 since it is a constant offset. In the ultra-relativistic case where we can ignore the particle mass, we find

$$E_n = |\Pi_n|c = \frac{n\pi\hbar c}{a} \quad \text{(zero mass).} \qquad (9.17)$$

The shapes of the wave functions for the first three values of n for the particle in the box are illustrated in figure 9.2.

In both limits the energy takes on only a certain set of possible values. This is called *energy quantization* and the integer n is called the *energy quantum number*. In the non-relativistic limit the energy is proportional to n^2, while in the ultra-relativistic case the energy is proportional to n.

We can graphically represent the allowed energy levels for the particle in a box by an *energy level diagram*. Such a diagram is shown in figure 9.3 for the non-relativistic case.

One aspect of this problem deserves a closer look. Equation (9.13) shows that the wave function for this problem is a superposition of two plane waves corresponding to momenta $\Pi_1 = +\hbar k$ and $\Pi_2 = -\hbar k$ and is therefore a kind of wave packet. Thus, the wave function is not invariant under displacement

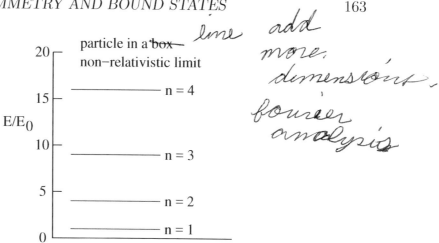

Figure 9.3: Allowed energy levels for the non-relativistic particle in a box. The constant $E_0 = \pi^2\hbar^2/(2ma^2)$. See text for the meanings of symbols.

and does not correspond to a definite value of the momentum — the momentum's absolute value is definite, but its sign is not. Following Feynman's prescription, equation (9.13) tells us that the amplitude for the particle in the box to have momentum $+\hbar k$ is $\exp[i(kx - \omega t)]$, while the amplitude for it to have momentum $-\hbar k$ is $-\exp[i(-kx - \omega t)]$. The absolute square of the sum of these amplitudes gives us the relative probability of finding the particle at position x:

$$P(x) = |2i\exp(-i\omega t)\sin(kx)|^2 = 4\sin^2(kx). \qquad (9.18)$$

Which of the two possible values of the momentum the particle takes on is unknowable, just as it is impossible in principle to know which slit a particle passes through in two slit interference. If an experiment is done to measure the momentum, then the wave function is irreversibly changed, just as the interference pattern in the two slit problem is destroyed if the slit through which the particle passes is unambiguously determined.

9.3.2   Barrier Penetration

Unlike the situation in classical mechanics, quantum mechanics allows the kinetic energy K to be negative. This makes the momentum Π (equal to

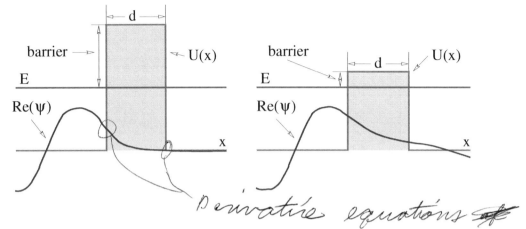

Figure 9.4: Real part of wave function $\text{Re}[\psi(x)]$ for barrier penetration. The left panel shows weak penetration occurring for a large potential energy barrier, while the right panel shows stronger penetration which occurs when the barrier is small.

$(2mK)^{1/2}$ in the nonrelativistic case) imaginary, which in turn gives rise to an imaginary wavenumber.

Let us investigate the nature of a wave with an imaginary wavenumber. Let us assume that $k = i\kappa$ in a complex exponential plane wave, where κ is real:

$$\psi = \exp[i(kx - \omega t)] = \exp(-\kappa x - i\omega t) = \exp(-\kappa x)\exp(-i\omega t). \qquad (9.19)$$

The wave function doesn't oscillate in space when $K = E - U < 0$, but grows or decays exponentially with x, depending on the sign of κ.

For a particle moving to the right, with positive k in the allowed region, κ turns out to be positive, and the solution decays to the right. Thus, a particle impingent on a potential energy barrier from the left (i. e., while moving to the right) will have its wave amplitude decay in the classically forbidden region, as illustrated in figure 9.4. If this decay is very rapid, then the result is almost indistinguishable from the classical result — the particle cannot penetrate into the forbidden region to any great extent. However, if the decay is slow, then there is a reasonable chance of finding the particle in the forbidden region. If the forbidden region is finite in extent, then the wave amplitude will be small, but non-zero at its right boundary, implying that the particle has a finite chance of completely passing through the classical forbidden region. This process is called *barrier penetration.*

The probability for a particle to penetrate a barrier is the absolute square of the amplitude after the barrier divided by the square of the amplitude before the barrier. Thus, in the case of the wave function illustrated in equation (9.19), the probability of penetration is

$$P = |\psi(d)|^2/|\psi(0)|^2 = \exp(-2\kappa d) \tag{9.20}$$

where d is the thickness of the barrier.

The rate of exponential decay with x in the forbidden region is related to how negative K is in this region. Since

$$-K = U - E = -\frac{\Pi^2}{2m} = -\frac{\hbar^2 k^2}{2m} = \frac{\hbar^2 \kappa^2}{2m}, \tag{9.21}$$

we find that

$$\kappa = \left(\frac{2mB}{\hbar^2}\right)^{1/2} \tag{9.22}$$

where the *potential energy barrier* is $B \equiv -K = U - E$. The smaller B is, the smaller is κ, resulting in less rapid decay of the wave function with x. This corresponds to stronger barrier penetration. (Note that the way B is defined, it is positive in forbidden regions.)

If the energy barrier is very high, then the exponential decay of the wave function is very rapid. In this case the wave function goes nearly to zero at the boundary between the allowed and forbidden regions. This is why we specify the wave function to be zero at the walls for the particle in a box. These walls act in effect as infinitely high potential barriers.

Barrier penetration is important in a number of natural phenomena. Certain types of radioactive decay and the fissioning of heavy nuclei are governed by this process.

9.3.3   Orbital Angular Momentum

Another type of bound state motion occurs when a particle is constrained to move in a circle. (Imagine a bead sliding on a circular loop of wire, as illustrated in figure 9.5.) We can define x in this case as the path length around the wire and relate it to the angle θ: $x = R\theta$. For a plane wave we have

$$\psi = \exp[i(kx - \omega t)] = \exp[i(kR\theta - \omega t)]. \tag{9.23}$$

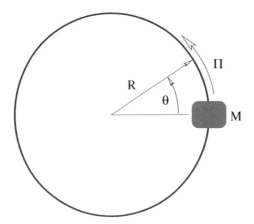

Figure 9.5: Illustration of a bead of mass M sliding (without friction) on a circular loop of wire of radius R with momentum Π.

This plane wave differs from the normal plane wave for motion along a Cartesian axis in that we must have $\psi(\theta) = \psi(\theta + 2\pi)$. This can only happen if the circumference of the loop, $2\pi R$, is an integral number of wavelengths, i. e., if $2\pi R/\lambda = m$ where m is an integer. However, since $2\pi/\lambda = k$, this condition becomes $kR = m$.

Since $\Pi = \hbar k$, the above condition can be written $\Pi_m R = m\hbar$. The quantity

$$L_m \equiv \Pi_m R \tag{9.24}$$

is called the *angular momentum*, leading to our final result,

$$L_m = m\hbar, \quad m = 0, \pm 1, \pm 2, \ldots. \tag{9.25}$$

We see that the angular momentum can only take on values which are integer multiples of $\hbar$. This represents the *quantization of angular momentum*, and m in this case is called the *angular momentum quantum number*. Note that this quantum number differs from the energy quantum number for the particle in the box in that zero and negative values are allowed.

The energy of our bead on a loop of wire can be expressed in terms of the angular momentum:

$$E_m = \frac{\Pi_m^2}{2M} = \frac{L_m^2}{2MR^2}. \tag{9.26}$$

This means that angular momentum and energy are compatible variables in this case, which further means that angular momentum is a conserved variable. Just as definite values of linear momentum are related to invariance under translations, definite values of angular momentum are related to invariance under rotations. Thus, we have

$$\text{invariance under rotation} \Longleftrightarrow \text{definite angular momentum} \qquad (9.27)$$

for angular momentum.

We need to briefly address the issue of angular momentum in three dimensions. Angular momentum is actually a vector oriented perpendicular to the wire loop in the example we are discussing. The direction of the vector is defined using a variation on the right-hand rule: Curl your fingers in the direction of motion of the bead around the loop (using your right hand!). The orientation of the angular momentum vector is defined by the direction in which your thumb points. This tells you, for instance, that the angular momentum in figure 9.5 points out of the page.

In quantum mechanics it is only possible to measure simultaneously the square of the length of the angular momentum vector and one component of this vector. Two different components of angular momentum cannot be simultaneously measured because of the uncertainty principle. However, the *length* of the angular momentum vector may be measured simultaneously with one component. Thus, in quantum mechanics, the angular momentum is completely specified if the length and one component of the angular momentum vector are known.

Figure 9.6 illustrates the angular momentum vector associated with a bead moving on a wire loop which is tilted from the horizontal. One component (taken to be the z component) is shown as well. For reasons we cannot explore here, the square of the length of the angular momentum vector L^2 is quantized with the following values:

$$L_l^2 = \hbar^2 l(l+1), \qquad l = 0, 1, 2, \ldots . \qquad (9.28)$$

One component (say, the z component) of angular momentum is quantized just like angular momentum in the two-dimensional case, except that l acts as an upper bound on the possible values of $|m|$. In other words, if the square of the length of the angular momentum vector is $\hbar^2 l(l+1)$, then the z component can take on the values

$$L_{zm} = \hbar m, \qquad m = -l, -l+1, \ldots, l-1, l. \qquad (9.29)$$

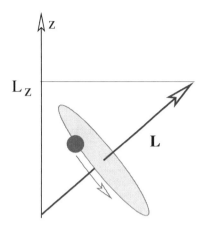

Figure 9.6: Illustration of the angular momentum vector **L** for a tilted loop and its z component L_z.

The quantity l is called the *angular momentum quantum number*, while m is called the *orientation* or *magnetic quantum number*, the latter for historical reasons.

9.3.4 Spin Angular Momentum

The type of angular momentum discussed above is associated with the movement of particles in orbits. However, it turns out that even stationary particles can possess angular momentum. This is called *spin* angular momentum. The *spin quantum number s* plays a role analogous to l for spin angular momentum, i. e., the square of the spin angular momentum vector of a particle is

$$L_s^2 = \hbar^2 s(s+1). \tag{9.30}$$

The *spin orientation quantum number m_s* is similarly related to s:

$$L_{zs} = \hbar m_s, \qquad m_s = -s, -s+1, \ldots, s-1, s. \tag{9.31}$$

The spin angular momentum for an elementary particle is absolutely conserved, i. e., it can never change. Thus, the value of s is an intrinsic property of a particle. The major difference between spin and orbital angular momentum is that the spin quantum number can take on more values, i. e., $s = 0, 1/2, 1, 3/2, 2, 5/2, \ldots$.

Particles with integer spin values $s = 0, 1, 2, \ldots$ are called *bosons* after the Indian physicist Satyendra Nath Bose. Particles with half-integer spin values $s = 1/2, 3/2, 5/2, \ldots$ are called *fermions* after the Italian physicist Enrico Fermi. As we shall see later in the course, bosons and fermions play very different roles in the universe.

9.4 Problems

1. Suppose that a particle is represented by the wave function $\psi = \sin(kx - \omega t) + \sin(-kx - \omega t)$.

   (a) Use trigonometry to simplify this wave function.

   (b) Compute the x and t dependence of the probability of finding the particle by squaring the wave function.

   (c) Explain what this result says about the time dependence of the probability of finding the particle. Does this make sense?

2. Repeat the above problem for a particle represented by the wave function $\psi = \exp[i(kx - \omega t)] + \exp[i(-kx - \omega t)]$.

3. Determine if the wavefunction $\psi(x) = \exp(iCx^2)$ is invariant under displacement in the sense that the displaced wave function differs from the original wave function by just a phase factor.

4. Just as invariance under the substitution $x \to x + D$ is associated with momentum, invariance under the substitution $x \to -x$ is associated with a quantum mechanical variable called *parity*, denoted P. However, unlike momentum, which can take on any numerical value, parity can take on only two possible values, ± 1. The parity of a wave function $\psi(x)$ is $+1$ if $\psi(-x) = \psi(x)$, while the parity is -1 if $\psi(-x) = -\psi(x)$. If $\psi(x)$ satisfies neither of these conditions, then it has no definite value of parity.

   (a) What is the parity of $\psi = \sin(kx)$? Of $\psi = \cos(kx)$? The quantity k is a constant.

   (b) Is $\psi(x) = \cos(kx)$ invariant under the substitution $x = x + D$ for all possible values of D? Does this wave function have a definite value of the momentum?

(c) Show that a wave function with a definite value of the momentum does not have a definite value of parity. Are momentum and parity compatible variables?

5. Realizing that $\cos(kx - \omega t)$ can be written in terms of complex exponential functions, give a physical interpretation of the meaning of the above cosine wave function. In particular, what are the possible values of the associated particle's momentum and energy?

6. The time reversal operation T makes the substitution $t \to -t$. Similar to parity, time reversal can only take on values ± 1. Is symmetry of a wave function under time reversal, i. e., $\psi(-t) = \psi(t)$, consistent with a definite value of the energy? Hint: Any wave function corresponding to a definite value of energy E must have the form $\psi = A \exp(-iEt/\hbar)$ where A is not a function of time t. (Why?)

7. The operation C takes the complex conjugate of the wave function, i. e., it makes the substitution $i \to -i$. In modern quantum mechanics this corresponds to interchanging particles and antiparticles, and is called *charge conjugation*. What does the combined operation CPT do to a complex plane wave, i. e., one with definite wave vector and frequency?

8. Make an energy level diagram for the case of a massless particle in a box.

9. Compare $|\Pi|$ for the ground state of a non-relativistic particle in a box of size a with $\Delta\Pi$ obtained from the uncertainty principle in this situation. Hint: What should you take for Δx?

10. Imagine that a billiard table has an infinitely high rim around it. For this problem assume that $\hbar = 1$ kg m^2 s^{-1}.

   (a) If the table is 1.5 m long and if the mass of a billiard ball is $M = 0.5$ kg, what is the billiard ball's lowest or ground state energy? Hint: Even though the billiard table is two dimensional, treat this as a one-dimensional problem. Also, treat the problem nonrelativistically and ignore the contribution of the rest energy to the total energy.

   (b) The energy required to lift the ball over a rim of height H against gravity is $U = MgH$ where $g = 9.8$ m s^{-2}. What rim height

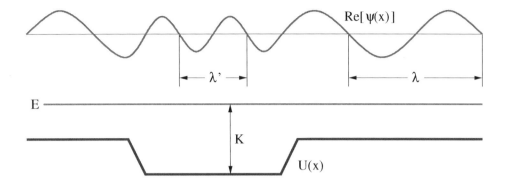

Figure 9.7: Real part of the wave function ψ, corresponding to a fixed total energy E, occurring in a region of spatially variable potential energy $U(x)$. Notice how the wavelength λ changes as the kinetic energy $K = E - U$ changes.

makes the gravitational potential energy equal to the ground state energy of the billiard ball calculated above?

(c) If the rim is actually twice as high as calculated above but is only 0.1 m thick, determine the probability of the ball penetrating the rim.

11. The real part of the wave function of a particle with positive energy E passing through a region of negative potential energy is shown in figure 9.7.

(a) If the total energy is definitely E, what is the dependence of this wave function on time?

(b) Is the wave function invariant under displacement in space in this case? Why or why not?

(c) Does this wave function correspond to a definite value of momentum? Why or why not?

(d) Is the momentum compatible with the energy in this case? Why or why not?

12. Assuming again that $\hbar = 1$ kg m^2 s^{-1}, what are the possible speeds

of a toy train of mass 3 kg running around a circular track of radius 0.8 m?

13. If a particle of zero mass sliding around a circular loop of radius R can take on angular momenta $L_m = m\hbar$ where m is an integer, what are the possible kinetic energies of the particle? Hint: Remember that $L = \Pi R$.

9.4) Parity (P)

$P = +1$ if $\psi(-x) = \psi(x)$

$P = -1$ if $\psi(-x) = -\psi(x)$

otherwise, P is not definite

a) P of $\psi = \sin kx$

P of $\psi = \cos kx$ $x \to -x$

$\psi = \sin[k(-x)] = -\sin kx \to P = -1$

$\psi = \cos[k(-x)] = \cos kx \to P = 1$

b) $\psi = \cos kx \to$ invariant?

$\psi(x+D) = \cos[k(x+D)]$

not invariant

invariant under displacement = definite momentum

ψ doesn't have definite momentum

c) $\psi_{(x)} = e^{ikx}$

$\psi_{(x+D)} = e^{ik(x+D)} = e^{ikx} e^{ikD} \to$ is invariant, has def momentum

$\psi_{(-x)} = e^{+k(x)} = e^{-kx}$

$e^{-kx} \neq e^{ikx} = e^{ikx}$

$\to$ no def P, P & momentum not compatible

points

Chapter 10

Dynamics of Multiple Particles

So far we have considered only the dynamics of a single particle subject to an externally imposed potential energy. The particle has no way of influencing this external agent. In the real world particles interact with each other. In this chapter we learn how this happens.

We first rewrite Newton's second law in terms of momentum. This is useful in the subsequent consideration of Newton's third law, which leads to the principle of the conservation of momentum. Collisions between particles and the behavior of rockets and conveyor belts are then studied as applications of the conservation laws to more than one particle.

10.1   Momentum and Newton's Second Law

Up to this point we have stated Newton's second law in its conventional form, $\mathbf{F} = m\mathbf{a}$. However, in the non-relativistic case $m\mathbf{a} = md\mathbf{u}/dt = d(m\mathbf{u})/dt$, so we can also write Newton's second law as

$$\mathbf{F} = \frac{d\mathbf{p}}{dt} \quad \text{(Newton's second law)} \tag{10.1}$$

where $\mathbf{p} = m\mathbf{u}$ is the non-relativistic kinetic momentum. This form of Newton's second law is actually closer to Newton's original statement of the law. It also has the advantage that it is correct even in the relativistic case when the relativistic definition of kinetic momentum, $\mathbf{p} = m\mathbf{u}/(1 - u^2/c^2)^{1/2}$ (as defined earlier), is substituted.

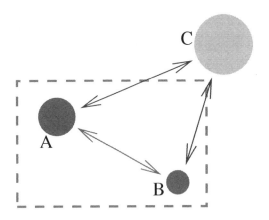

Figure 10.1: Interactions between three particles, A, B, and C. A and B are considered to be part of the system defined by the dashed line.

10.2 Newton's Third Law

Newton's third law states that if particle A exerts a force $\mathbf{F}$ on particle B, then particle B exerts a force $-\mathbf{F}$ on particle A. Newton's third law makes it possible to apply Newton's second law to systems of particles without considering the detailed interactions between particles within the system. For instance, if we (arbitrarily) define the system in figure 10.1 to be the particles A and B inside the dashed lines, then we can divide the forces acting on these particles into internal and external parts,

$$\mathbf{F}_A = \mathbf{F}_{A-internal} + \mathbf{F}_{A-external} = \frac{d\mathbf{p}_A}{dt}, \qquad (10.2)$$

$$\mathbf{F}_B = \mathbf{F}_{B-internal} + \mathbf{F}_{B-external} = \frac{d\mathbf{p}_B}{dt}. \qquad (10.3)$$

Adding these equations together results in the net force $\mathbf{F}_{net}$ being equal to

$$\mathbf{F}_{A-internal} + \mathbf{F}_{A-external} + \mathbf{F}_{B-internal} + \mathbf{F}_{B-external} = \frac{d}{dt}(\mathbf{p}_A + \mathbf{p}_B). \quad (10.4)$$

However, the internal interactions in this case are A acting on B and B acting on A. These forces are equal in magnitude but opposite in direction, so they cancel out, leaving us with the net force equal to the sum of the external parts, $\mathbf{F}_{net} = \mathbf{F}_{A-external} + \mathbf{F}_{B-external}$. The external forces in figure 10.1 are the force of C on A and the force of C on B. Defining the total kinetic momentum of the system as the sum of the A and B momenta, $\mathbf{p}_{tot} = \mathbf{p}_A + \mathbf{p}_B$, the above equation becomes

$$\mathbf{F}_{net} = \frac{d\mathbf{p}_{tot}}{dt}, \tag{10.5}$$

which looks just like Newton's second law for a single particle, except that it now applies to the system of particles (A and B in the present case) as a whole. This argument easily generalizes to any number of particles inside and outside the system. Thus, for instance, even though a soccer ball consists of billions of atoms, we are sure that the forces between atoms within the soccer ball cancel out, and the trajectory of the ball as a whole is determined solely by external forces such as gravity, wind drag, friction with the ground, and the kicks of soccer players.

Remember that for two forces to be a third law pair, they have to be acting on different particles. Furthermore, if one member of the pair is the force of particle A acting on particle B, then the other must be the force of particle B acting on particle A. A counterexample would be gravity and the upward normal force acting on a mass sitting on a table; these forces are equal and opposite in the stationary case, but act on the same object, and therefore *do not* constitute a third law pair. However, the upward normal force of the table on the mass and the downward normal force of the mass on the table *would be* a third law pair.

10.3   Conservation of Momentum

If all external forces on a system are zero, then equation (10.5) reduces to

$$\mathbf{p}_{tot} = const \quad \text{(isolated system)}. \tag{10.6}$$

A system of particles with no external forces acting on it is called *isolated*. Newton's third law thus tells us that the kinetic momentum of an isolated system doesn't change with time. This law is called the *conservation of momentum*.

10.4 Collisions

Let us now consider the situation in which two particles collide with each other. There can be several outcomes to this collision, of which we will study two:

- The two particles collide *elastically*, in essence bouncing off of each other.

- The two particles stick together, resulting in the production of a single particle, or a single particle breaks apart into two particles. These are *inelastic processes*.

In both of the above cases energy and momentum are conserved. We assume that the forces acting between the particles are short range, so that except in the instant of collision, we need not worry about potential energy or potential momentum — all energy is in the form of rest plus kinetic energy except in this short interval, and all momenta are kinetic momenta.

Because of the principle of relativity, we are free to consider collisions in any convenient reference frame. We can then transform the results to any reference frame we please. Generally speaking, the most convenient reference frame to consider is the one in which the total momentum of the two particles is zero. For the sake of simplicity we only consider collisions in one dimension.

10.4.1 Elastic Collisions

Suppose a particle with mass m_1 and initial velocity u_1 in the *center of momentum* frame, i. e., the reference frame in which the total momentum is zero, collides elastically with another particle of mass m_2 with initial velocity u_2. The momenta of the two particles are

$$p_1 = \frac{m_1 u_1}{(1 - u_1^2/c^2)^{1/2}} \quad p_2 = \frac{m_2 u_2}{(1 - u_2^2/c^2)^{1/2}}. \tag{10.7}$$

In the center of momentum frame we must have

$$p_1 = -p_2. \tag{10.8}$$

Figure 10.2 shows what happens when these two particles collide. The first particle acquires momentum p_1' while the second acquires momentum

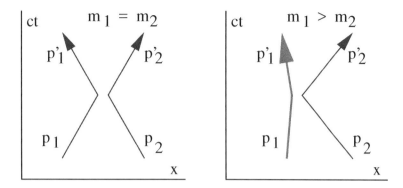

Figure 10.2: One-dimensional elastic collisions of two particles in the center of momentum frame as seen in spacetime diagrams.

---

p_2'. The conservation of momentum tells us that the total momentum after the collision is the same as before the collision, namely zero, so

$$p_1' = -p_2'. \tag{10.9}$$

In the center of momentum frame we know that $|p_1| = |p_2|$ and we know that the two momentum vectors point in opposite directions. Similarly, $|p_1'| = |p_2'|$. However, we as yet don't know how p_1' is related to p_1. Conservation of energy,

$$E_1 + E_2 = E_1' + E_2', \tag{10.10}$$

gives us this information. Notice that if $p_1' = -p_1$, then $E_1'^2 = p_1'^2c^2 + m_1^2c^4 = p_1^2c^2 + m_1^2c^4 = E_1^2$. Assuming positive energies, we therefore have $E_1' = E_1$. If $p_2' = -p_2$, then we can similarly infer that $E_2' = E_2$. If these conditions are satisfied, then so is equation (10.10). Therefore, a complete solution to the problem is

$$p_1 = -p_1' = -p_2 = p_2' \equiv p \tag{10.11}$$

and

$$E_1 = E_1' = (p^2c^2 + m_1^2c^4)^{1/2} \quad E_2 = E_2' = (p^2c^2 + m_2^2c^4)^{1/2}. \tag{10.12}$$

In other words, the particles just exchange momenta.

The left panel of figure 10.2 shows what happens in a collision when the masses of the two colliding particles are equal. If $m_1 = m_2$, then the incoming

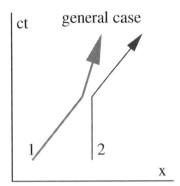
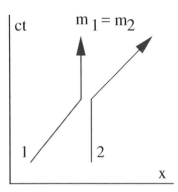

Figure 10.3: Elastic collisions viewed from a reference frame in which one particle is initially stationary.

and outgoing velocities of the two particles are the same, as indicated by the inverse slopes of the world lines. On the other hand, if $m_1 > m_2$, then the velocity of particle 2 is greater than the velocity of particle 1, as is illustrated in the right panel of figure 10.2.

Suppose we wish to view the results of an elastic collision in a reference frame in which particle 2 is initially stationary. All we have to do is to transform the velocities into a reference frame moving with the initial velocity of particle 2, as illustrated in figure 10.3. We do this by relativistically adding $U = -u_2$ to each velocity. (Note that the velocity U of the moving frame is positive since u_2 is negative.) Using the relativistic velocity translation formula, we find that

$$v_1 = \frac{u_1 + U}{1 + u_1 U/c^2} \quad v_1' = \frac{u_1' + U}{1 + u_1' U/c^2} \quad v_2' = \frac{u_2' + U}{1 + u_2' U/c^2} \qquad (10.13)$$

where u_1, u_1', u_2, and u_2' indicate velocities in the original, center of momentum reference frame and v_1, v_1', etc., indicate velocities in the transformed frame.

In the special case where the masses of the two particles are equal to each other, we have $v_1 = 2U/(1 + U^2/c^2)$, $v_1' = 0$, and $v_2' = 2U/(1 + U^2/c^2) = v_1$. Thus, when the masses are equal, the particles simply exchange velocities.

If the velocities are nonrelativistic, then the simpler Galilean transformation law $v = u + U$ can be used in place of the relativistic equations invoked above.

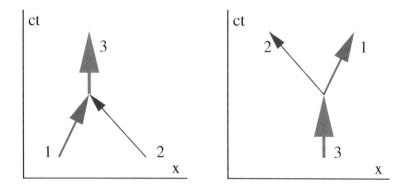

Figure 10.4: Building blocks of inelastic collisions. In the left panel two particles collide to form a third particle. In the right panel a particle breaks up, forming two particles.

10.4.2 Inelastic Collisions

An inelastic collision is one in which the particles coming out of the collision are not the same as the particles going into it. Inelastic collisions conserve both total momentum and energy just as elastic collisions do. However, unlike elastic collisions, inelastic collisions generally do not conserve the total *kinetic* energy of the particles, as some rest energy is generally created or destroyed.

Figure 10.4 shows the fundamental building blocks of inelastic collisions. We can consider even the most complex inelastic collisions to be made up of composites of only two processes, the creation of one particle from two, and the disintegration of one particle into two.

Let us consider each of these in the center of momentum frame. In both cases the single particle must be stationary in this frame since it carries the total momentum of the system, which has to be zero. By conservation of momentum, if particle 1 in the left panel of figure 10.4 has momentum p, then the momentum of particle 2 is $-p$. If the two particles have masses m_1 and m_2, then their energies are $E_1 = (p^2c^2 + m_1^2c^4)^{1/2}$ and $E_2 = (p^2c^2 + m_2^2c^4)^{1/2}$. The energy of particle 3 is therefore $E_3 = E_1 + E_2$, and since it is at rest, all of its energy is in the form of "mc^2" or rest energy, and so the mass of this particle is

$$m_3 = (E_1 + E_2)/c^2 \quad \text{(center of momentum frame)}$$

$$\begin{aligned}
&= (p^2/c^2 + m_1^2)^{1/2} + (p^2/c^2 + m_2^2)^{1/2}\\
&= m_1[1 + p^2/(m_1^2c^2)]^{1/2} + m_2[1 + p^2/(m_2^2c^2)]^{1/2}. \quad (10.14)
\end{aligned}$$

The last line in the above equation shows that $m_3 > m_1 + m_2$ because it is in the form $m_1A + m_2B$ where both A and B are greater than one. Thus, rest energy is created in the amount $\Delta E_{rest} = (m_3 - m_1 - m_2)c^2$.

Actually, it is easy to calculate the mass of particle 3 in the above case from any reference frame as long as the momenta and energies of particles 1 and 2 are known in this frame. By conservation of energy and momentum, $E_3 = E_1 + E_2$ and $\mathbf{p}_3 = \mathbf{p}_1 + \mathbf{p}_2$. Furthermore, $E_3^2 = p_3^2c^2 + m_3^2c^4$, so we can solve for m_3:

$$m_3 = [(E_1 + E_2)^2/c^4 - (\mathbf{p}_1 + \mathbf{p}_2) \cdot (\mathbf{p}_1 + \mathbf{p}_2)/c^2]^{1/2} \quad \text{(any frame).} \quad (10.15)$$

The right panel of figure 10.4 shows the process of particle decay. This is just the inverse of the particle creation process, and all of the analysis we have done for creation is valid for particle decay except that rest energy is converted to kinetic energy rather than vice versa.

10.5 Rockets and Conveyor Belts

Normally when we define a system to which Newton's second law is to be applied, the system is *closed* in the sense that mass cannot enter or exit the system. However, sometimes it is convenient to work with *open* systems for which this is not true. The classic example is the rocket, where exhaust gases leave the system, thus decreasing the mass of the rocket with time.

Open systems can be analyzed if momentum is considered to be a quantity which is accounted for much as money is accounted for in a bank account. The bank account can change in three ways: money can be deposited in the account, it can be withdrawn from the account, and the amount can grow or shrink as a consequence of interest payments or fees. Similarly, the amount of momentum in a system can change as the result of mass entering the system, mass leaving the system, and forces acting on the system. The time rate of change of momentum in a system is therefore

$$\frac{dp}{dt} = F + \left(\frac{dp}{dt}\right)_{in} - \left(\frac{dp}{dt}\right)_{out}, \quad (10.16)$$

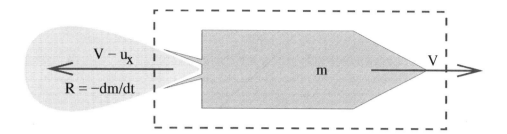

Figure 10.5: Rocket moving with velocity V while expelling gas at a rate R with velocity $V - u_x$.

---

where F is the net force on the system, $(dp/dt)_{in}$ is the momentum per unit time added by mass entering the system, and $(dp/dt)_{out}$ is the amount lost per unit time by mass exiting the system. In the non-relativistic case, $(dp/dt)_{in} = u_{in}(dm/dt)_{in}$ and $(dp/dt)_{out} = u_{out}(dm/dt)_{out}$, where $(dm/dt)_{in}$ is the mass entering the system per unit time with velocity u_{in} and $(dm/dt)_{out}$ is the mass per unit time exiting the system with velocity u_{out}.

For non-relativistic velocities, the momentum of the system can be written as $p = mu$ so that

$$\frac{dp}{dt} = \frac{dm}{dt}u + m\frac{du}{dt}. \tag{10.17}$$

To complete the analysis, we need an accounting of the mass entering and leaving the system:

$$\frac{dm}{dt} = \left(\frac{dm}{dt}\right)_{in} - \left(\frac{dm}{dt}\right)_{out}. \tag{10.18}$$

Let us see how to apply this to a rocket for which all velocities are non-relativistic. As figure 10.5 indicates, a rocket spews out a stream of exhaust gas. The system is defined by the dashed box and includes the rocket and the part of the exhaust gas inside the box. The reaction to the momentum carried off in this stream of gas is what causes the rocket to accelerate. We note that $(dm/dt)_{in} = 0$ since no mass is entering the system, and $(dm/dt)_{out} = R$, the rate at which mass is ejected by the rocket in the form of exhaust gas. The rocket is assumed to be moving to the right at speed V and the gas is ejected at a speed u_x relative to the rocket, which means that its actual velocity after ejection is $V - u_x$. We call u_x the *exhaust velocity*. Notice that $V - u_x$ may be either positive or negative, depending on how big V is.

Equating the mass of the rocket to the system mass, we find that $R = -dm/dt$. The momentum balance equation (10.16) becomes $dp/dt = -(V - u_x)R$. The force on the rocket is actually zero, so the force term does not enter the momentum balance equation. This is non-intuitive, because we are used to acceleration being the result of a force. However, nothing, including the ejected gas, is actually *pushing* on the system, so we must indeed conclude that there is no force — all of the change in the system's momentum arises from the ejection of gas with the opposite momentum.[1]

Finally, we see that $dp/dt = (dm/dt)V + m(dV/dt) = -RV + m(dV/dt)$. Equating this to the results of the momentum balance calculation gives us $-RV + m(dV/dt) = -(V - u_x)R$. Solving for the acceleration dV/dt results in

$$\frac{dV}{dt} = \frac{u_x R}{m} \quad \text{(rocket acceleration).} \tag{10.19}$$

Thus, the acceleration of the rocket depends on the exhaust velocity of the ejected gas, the rate at which the gas is being ejected, and the mass of the rocket.

Figure 10.6 illustrates another type of open system problem. A hopper dumps sand on a conveyor belt at a rate of R kilograms per second. The conveyor belt is moving to the right at (non-relativistic) speed V and the sand is dumped off at the end. What force F is needed to keep the conveyor belt moving at a constant speed, assuming that the conveyor belt mechanism itself is frictionless? In this case $(dm/dt)_{in} = (dm/dt)_{out} = R$. Furthermore, since the system outlined by the dashed line is in a steady state, $dp/dt = 0$.

The key to understanding this problem is that the sand enters the system with zero horizontal velocity, but exits the system with the horizontal velocity of the conveyor belt, V. The momentum balance equation is thus

$$0 = F - VR \tag{10.20}$$

and the force is

$$F = VR \quad \text{(force on conveyor belt).} \tag{10.21}$$

---

[1]The back pressure of the gas outside the system on the gas inside the system is negligible once the gas exits the nozzle of the rocket engine. If we took the inside of the combustion chamber to be part of the system boundary, the results would be different, as the gas pressure there is non-negligible. At this point the gas is indeed exerting a significant force on the rocket. However, though this viewpoint is *conceptually* simpler, it is *computationally* more difficult, which is why we define the system as we do.

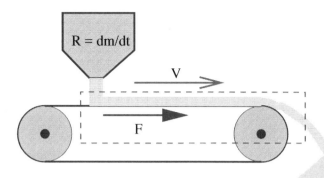

Figure 10.6: Sand is dumped on a conveyor belt and in turn is dumped off the end of the belt.

This force serves to accelerate the sand up to the velocity of the conveyor belt.

10.6   Problems

1. Imagine a block of mass M resting on a plate under the influence of gravity, as shown in figure 10.7.

   (a) Determine the force of the plate on the block, $\mathbf{N}_b$, and the force of the block on the plate, $\mathbf{N}_p$.

   (b) State which of the three forces, $M\mathbf{g}$, $\mathbf{N}_b$, and $\mathbf{N}_p$, form a Newton's third law pair.

2. Repeat the previous problem assuming that the block and the plate are in an elevator accelerating upward with acceleration $\mathbf{a}$.

3. Straighten out the misunderstanding of Newton's third law implicit in the question "If the force of the horse on the cart equals the force of the cart on the horse, why does anything ever go anywhere"? Examine in particular the conditions under which the horse-cart system accelerates.

4. A pusher boat (mass M) on the Mississippi is pushing two barges (each mass m) at a steady speed as shown in figure 10.8. Each barge is

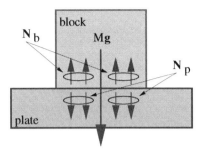

Figure 10.7: Block of mass M subject to gravitational force $M\mathbf{g}$ while resting on a plate. The force of the block on the plate is $\mathbf{N}_p$ while the force of the plate on the block is $\mathbf{N}_b$.

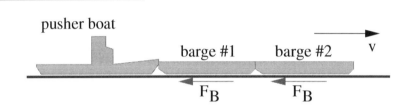

Figure 10.8: Barges being pushed by a pusher boat on the Mississippi. Each barge experiences a drag force F_b.

subject to a drag force by the water of F_B. Consider only horizontal force components in the following.

(a) What is the total horizontal force of the water on the barge-boat system? Explain.

(b) What is the direction and magnitude of the force of the pusher boat on barge 1? Explain.

5. A train with an engine of mass M and 2 freight cars, each of mass m, is accelerating to the right with acceleration a on a horizontal track as shown in figure 10.9. Assume that the two freight cars roll with negligible friction. Consider only horizontal force components below.

(a) Find the direction and magnitude of the force of the rails on the

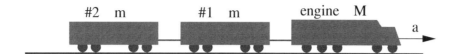

Figure 10.9: An engine and two freight cars accelerating to the right.

engine and specify the system to which Newton's second law is applied.

(b) Find the direction and magnitude of the force of the engine on the first car and specify the system to which Newton's second law is applied.

(c) Find the direction and magnitude of the force of the first car on the second car and specify the system to which Newton's second law is applied.

(d) Find the direction and magnitude of the force of the second car on the first car and specify the law used to obtain this force.

6. A car and trailer are descending a hill as shown in figure 10.10. Assume that the trailer rolls without friction and that air friction can be ignored. Consider only forces parallel to the road surface.

(a) Compute the force of the road on the car if the car-trailer system shown in figure 10.10 is moving down the hill at constant speed.

(b) Compute the force of the trailer on the car in the above conditions.

(c) If the driver takes his foot off the brake and lets the car coast frictionlessly, recompute the force of the trailer on the car.

7. Consider a one-dimensional elastic collision between particles of masses m_1 and m_2. If particle 2 is initially stationary, what range of values must m_1/m_2 have for the initial particle to rebound backwards along its initial track after the collision? (Do this problem non-relativistically.)

8. A stationary pion (mass M) decays into a muon (mass $m < M$) and a neutrino (massless).

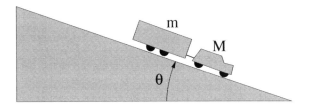

Figure 10.10: A car and a trailer going down a hill.

___

    (a) What is the (fully relativistic) momentum of the muon after the decay?

    (b) What is the energy of the neutrino?

9. In an elastic collision viewed in the center of momentum frame, the energy of each particle is conserved individually. Is this true for the same process viewed from a reference frame in which one of the particles is initially stationary?

10. A space probe approaches a planet in the $-x$ direction, curves around it under the influence of the planet's powerful gravity (a conservative force) and recedes from the planet in the $+x$ direction, as seen in figure 10.11. The planet is moving in the $+x$ direction at speed V, while the space probe is initially moving in the $-x$ direction at speed u_1. What is its speed u_2 in the $+x$ direction after this close approach to the planet? Treat this problem nonrelativistically. Hint: First transform to the center of mass frame in which the planet is essentially stationary. Work out the interaction between the probe and the planet in this frame. Then transform back to the original reference frame. Assume that the mass of the probe is negligible compared to that of the planet.

11. Two asteroids, each with mass 10^{10} kg and initial speed 10^5 m s^{-1}, collide head on. The whole mess congeals into one large mass. How much rest mass (rest energy divided by c^2) is created?

12. Two equal objects, both with mass m, collide and stick together. Before the collision, one mass is stationary and the other is moving at speed v. In the following, assume that velocities are fully relativistic.

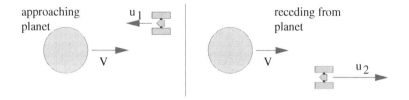

Figure 10.11: A space probe approaches a planet, curves around it, and heads off in the opposite direction.

    (a) Compute the total momentum and energy (including rest energy) of the two masses before the collision.

    (b) Compute the mass M of the combined system after the collision, taking the conversion of energy into mass into account.

13. Explain qualitatively why a fireman needs to push forward on a firehose to keep it stationary. Hint: The water is flowing faster after it comes out of the nozzle of the hose than before.

14. Solve equation (10.19) for V as a function of m, assuming that $V = 0$ and $m = m_0$ at $t = 0$. Hint: Since $R = -dm/dt$, we have $R/m = -d\ln(m)/dt$.

15. Bottles are filled with soft drink at a bottling plant as shown in figure 10.12. The bottles sit on a scale which is used to determine when to shut off the flow of soft drink. If the desired mass of the bottle plus soft drink after filling is M, what weight should the scale read when the bottle is full? The rate at which mass is being added to the bottle is R and its velocity entering the bottle is V.

16. An interstellar space probe has frontal area A, initial mass M_0, and initial velocity V_0, which is non-relativistic. The tenuous gas between the stars has mass density ρ. These gas molecules stick to the probe when they hit it. Find the probe's acceleration. Hint: In a frame of reference in which the gas is stationary, does the momentum of the space probe change with time? Does its mass?

17. A light beam with power J hits a plate which is oriented normally to the beam. Compute the force required to hold the plate in place if

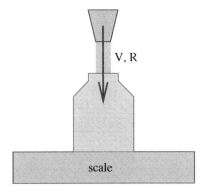

Figure 10.12: A bottle being filled with soft drink at a rate R. The liquid enters the bottle with velocity V.

___

   (a) the plate completely absorbs the light, and

   (b) the plate completely reflects the light.

Hint: Photons are massless, so the momentum of a photon with energy E is E/c. Thus, the momentum per unit time hitting the plate is J/c.

18. Find the acceleration of a rocket when the exhaust "gas" is actually a laser beam of power J. Assume that the rocket moves at non-relativistic velocities and that the decrease in mass due to the loss of energy in the laser beam is negligible.

Chapter 11

Rotational Dynamics

We have already seen the quantum mechanical treatment of angular momentum and rotational dynamics. In this section we study these subjects in a classical, non-relativistic context. We first define the concepts of torque and angular momentum in order to understand the orbital motion of a single particle. Next we examine two particles in arbitrary motion and learn how kinetic energy and angular momentum are partitioned between orbital and internal components. Two particles fixed to the ends of a light rod constitute a dumbbell, which serves as a prototype for the rotation of rigid bodies. We then see how what we learned for two particles extends to an arbitrary number of particles. Finally, we explore the physics of structures in static equilibrium.

Before we begin, we need to extend our knowledge of vectors to the cross product.

11.1 Math Tutorial — Cross Product

There are two ways to multiply two vectors together, the dot product and the cross product. We have already studied the dot product of two vectors, which results in a scalar or single number.

The cross product of two vectors results in a third vector, and is written symbolically as follows:

$$\mathbf{C} = \mathbf{A} \times \mathbf{B}. \tag{11.1}$$

As illustrated in figure 11.1, the cross product of two vectors is perpendicular to the plane defined by these vectors. However, this doesn't tell us

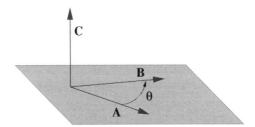

Figure 11.1: Illustration of the cross product of two vectors **A** and **B**. The resulting vector **C** is perpendicular to the plane defined by **A** and **B**.

---

whether the resulting vector in figure 11.1 points upward out of the plane or downward. This ambiguity is resolved using the *right-hand rule*:

1. Point the uncurled fingers of your right hand along the direction of the first vector **A**.

2. Rotate your arm until you can curl your fingers in the direction of the second vector **B**.

3. Your stretched out thumb now points in the direction of the cross product vector **C**.

The magnitude of the cross product is given by

$$|\mathbf{C}| = |\mathbf{A}||\mathbf{B}|\sin(\theta), \tag{11.2}$$

where $|\mathbf{A}|$ and $|\mathbf{B}|$ are the magnitudes of **A** and **B**, and θ is the angle between these two vectors. Note that the magnitude of the cross product is zero when the vectors are parallel or anti-parallel, and maximum when they are perpendicular. This contrasts with the dot product, which is maximum for parallel vectors and zero for perpendicular vectors.

Notice that the cross product does not commute, i. e., the order of the vectors is important. In particular, it is easy to show using the right-hand rule that

$$\mathbf{A} \times \mathbf{B} = -\mathbf{B} \times \mathbf{A}. \tag{11.3}$$

An alternate way to compute the cross product is most useful when the two vectors are expressed in terms of components, i. e., $\mathbf{A} = (A_x, A_y. A_z)$ and

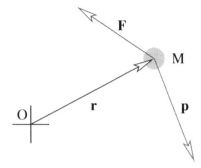

Figure 11.2: A mass M located at $\mathbf{r}$ relative to the origin O has momentum $\mathbf{p}$ and has a force $\mathbf{F}$ applied to it. By the right-hand rule the torque $\boldsymbol{\tau} = \mathbf{r} \times \mathbf{F}$ points out of the page, while the angular momentum $\mathbf{L} = \mathbf{r} \times \mathbf{p}$ points into the page.

$\mathbf{B} = (B_x, B_y, B_z)$:

$$\begin{aligned} C_x &= A_y B_z - A_z B_y \\ C_y &= A_z B_x - A_x B_z \\ C_z &= A_x B_y - A_y B_x. \end{aligned} \tag{11.4}$$

Notice that once you have the first of these equations, the other two can be obtained by cyclically permuting the indices, i. e., $x \to y$, $y \to z$, and $z \to x$. This is useful as a memory aid.

11.2   Torque and Angular Momentum

Torque is the action of a force $\mathbf{F}$ on a mass M which induces it to revolve about some point, called the *origin*. It is defined

$$\boldsymbol{\tau} = \mathbf{r} \times \mathbf{F}, \tag{11.5}$$

where $\mathbf{r}$ is the position of the mass relative to the origin, as illustrated in figure 11.2.

Notice that the torque is zero in a number of circumstances. If the force points directly toward or away from the origin, the cross product is zero, resulting in zero torque, even though the force is non-zero. Likewise, if

$\mathbf{r} = 0$, the torque is zero. Thus, a force acting at the origin produces no torque. Both of these limits make sense intuitively, since neither induces the mass to revolve around the origin.

The *angular momentum* of a mass M relative to a point O is

$$\mathbf{L} = \mathbf{r} \times \mathbf{p}, \tag{11.6}$$

where $\mathbf{p}$ is the ordinary kinetic momentum of the mass.[1] The angular momentum is zero if the motion of the object is directly towards or away from the origin, or if it is located at the origin.

If we take the cross product of the position vector and Newton's second law, we obtain an equation that relates torque and angular momentum:

$$\mathbf{r} \times \mathbf{F} = \mathbf{r} \times \frac{d\mathbf{p}}{dt} = \frac{d}{dt}(\mathbf{r} \times \mathbf{p}) - \frac{d\mathbf{r}}{dt} \times \mathbf{p}. \tag{11.7}$$

The second term on the right side of the above equation is zero because $d\mathbf{r}/dt$ equals the velocity of the mass, which is parallel to its momentum and the cross product of two parallel vectors is zero. This equation can therefore be written

$$\boldsymbol{\tau} = \frac{d\mathbf{L}}{dt} \quad \text{(Newton's second law for rotation)}. \tag{11.8}$$

It is the rotational version of Newton's second law.

For both torque and angular momentum the location of the origin is arbitrary, and is generally chosen for maximum convenience. However, it is necessary to choose the same origin for both the torque and the angular momentum.

For the case of a *central force*, i. e., one which acts along the line of centers between two objects (such as gravity), there often exists a particularly convenient choice of origin. Imagine a planet revolving around the sun, as illustrated in figure 11.3. If the origin is placed at the center of the sun (which is assumed not to move under the influence of the planet's gravity), then the torque exerted on the planet by the sun's gravity is zero, which means that the angular momentum of the planet about the center of the sun is constant in time. No other choice of origin would yield this convenient result.

---

[1]In the presence of a potential momentum we would have to distinguish between total and kinetic momentum. This in turn would lead to a distinction between total and kinetic angular momentum. We will assume that no potential momentum exists here, so that this distinction need not be made.

Figure 11.3: A convenient choice of origin for a planet (right-hand sphere) revolving around the sun is simply the center of the sun. In this case the torque of the sun's gravitational force on the planet is zero.

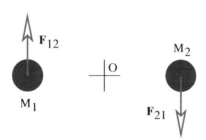

Figure 11.4: Scenario for the non-conservation of angular momentum. $\mathbf{F}_{12}$ is the force of mass M_2 on mass M_1 and vice versa.

We already know about two fundamental conservation laws — those of energy and linear momentum. We believe that angular momentum is similarly conserved in isolated systems. In other words, particles can exchange angular momentum between themselves, but the vector sum of the angular momentum of all the particles in a system isolated from outside influences must remain constant.

Conservation of angular momentum is not an automatic consequence of the conservation of linear momentum, even though the governing equation (11.8) for angular momentum is derived from Newton's second law. As an

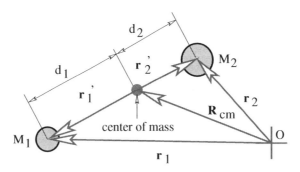

Figure 11.5: Two particles of mass M_1 and M_2 with $M_2 > M_1$.

example, figure 11.4 shows a hypothetical situation in which the force $\mathbf{F}_{21}$ of M_1 on M_2 is equal in magnitude but opposite in sign to the force $\mathbf{F}_{12}$ of M_2 on M_1, i. e., Newton's third law holds, and the sum of the momenta of the two masses is conserved. However, because the forces are non-central, the angular momentum of the masses is not conserved. This scenario is impossible if the forces are central.

11.3 Two Particles

Suppose we wish to apply Newton's second law to two particles considered together as a single system. As we showed previously, only external forces act on the total momentum, $\mathbf{p}_{total} = \mathbf{p}_1 + \mathbf{p}_2$, of the two particles:

$$\mathbf{F}_{external} = \frac{d\mathbf{p}_{total}}{dt}. \tag{11.9}$$

Let's write the total non-relativistic momentum of the two particles in a special way:

$$\mathbf{p}_{total} = M_1\mathbf{v}_1 + M_2\mathbf{v}_2 = M_{total}\left(\frac{M_1\mathbf{v}_1 + M_2\mathbf{v}_2}{M_{total}}\right) \equiv M_{total}\mathbf{V}_{cm}, \tag{11.10}$$

where $M_{total} = M_1 + M_2$. The quantity $\mathbf{V}_{cm}$ is the *velocity of the center of mass* and can be expressed as the time derivative of the *position of the center of mass*, $\mathbf{R}_{cm}$,

$$\mathbf{V}_{cm} = \frac{d\mathbf{R}_{cm}}{dt}, \tag{11.11}$$

where

$$\mathbf{R}_{cm} = \frac{M_1\mathbf{r}_1 + M_2\mathbf{r}_2}{M_{total}}. \tag{11.12}$$

We now see how the kinetic energy and the angular momentum of the two particles may be split into two parts, one having to do with the motion of the center of mass of the two particles, the other having to do with the motion of the two particles relative their center of mass. Figure 11.5 shows graphically how the vectors $\mathbf{r}_1' = \mathbf{r}_1 - \mathbf{R}_{cm}$ and $\mathbf{r}_2' = \mathbf{r}_2 - \mathbf{R}_{cm}$ are defined. These vectors represent the positions of the two particles relative to the center of mass. Substitution into equation (11.12) shows that $M_1\mathbf{r}_1' + M_2\mathbf{r}_2' = 0$. This leads to the conclusion that $M_1d_1 = M_2d_2$ in figure 11.5. We also define the velocity of each mass relative to the center of mass as $\mathbf{v}_1' = d\mathbf{r}_1'/dt$ and $\mathbf{v}_2' = d\mathbf{r}_2'/dt$, and we therefore have $M_1\mathbf{v}_1' + M_2\mathbf{v}_2' = 0$.

The total kinetic energy is just the sum of the kinetic energies of the two particles, $K = M_1v_1^2/2 + M_2v_2^2/2$, where v_1 and v_2 are the magnitudes of the corresponding velocity vectors. Substitution of $\mathbf{v}_1 = \mathbf{V}_{cm} + \mathbf{v}_1'$ etc., into the kinetic energy formula and rearranging yields

$$K_{total} = K_{trans} + K_{intern} = [M_{total}V_{cm}^2/2] + [M_1v_1'^2/2 + M_2v_2'^2/2]. \tag{11.13}$$

Terms like $\mathbf{V}_{cm} \cdot \mathbf{v}_1'$ cancel out because $M_1\mathbf{v}_1' + M_2\mathbf{v}_2' = 0$.

The first term on the right side of equation (11.13) in square brackets is the kinetic energy the two particles would have if all of the mass were concentrated at the center of mass. The second term is the kinetic energy computed relative to the motion of the center of mass. The first is called the *translational kinetic energy* of the system while the second is called the *internal kinetic energy*.

The angular momentum of the system is just the sum of the angular momenta of the two particles: $\mathbf{L}_{total} = M_1\mathbf{r}_1 \times \mathbf{v}_1 + M_2\mathbf{r}_2 \times \mathbf{v}_2$. By reasoning similar to the case of kinetic energy, we can rewrite this as

$$\mathbf{L}_{total} = \mathbf{L}_{orb} + \mathbf{L}_{spin} = [M_{total}\mathbf{R}_{cm} \times \mathbf{V}_{cm}] + [M_1\mathbf{r}_1' \times \mathbf{v}_1' + M_2\mathbf{r}_2' \times \mathbf{v}_2']. \tag{11.14}$$

The first term in square brackets on the right is called the *orbital angular momentum* while the second term is called the *spin angular momentum*. The former is the angular momentum the system would have if all the mass were concentrated at the center of mass, while the latter is the angular momentum of motion about the center of mass.

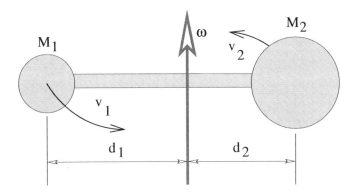

Figure 11.6: Perspective view of the rotating dumbbell attached to an axle labeled ω. The axle attaches to the crossbar at the center of mass. The velocity $\mathbf{v}_1$ is out of the page and $\mathbf{v}_2$ is into the page.

Interestingly, the idea of center of mass and the corresponding split of kinetic energy and angular momentum into orbital and spin parts has no useful relativistic generalization. This is due to the factor of $\gamma \equiv (1 - v^2/c^2)^{-1/2}$ in the relativistic definition of momentum, $\mathbf{p} = m\mathbf{v}\gamma$, which means that

$$\frac{dm\mathbf{r}}{dt} \neq \mathbf{p} \quad \text{(relativistic case)}. \tag{11.15}$$

11.4 The Uneven Dumbbell

So far we have put no restrictions on the movements of the two particles. An interesting special case occurs when the particles are connected by a lightweight, rigid rod, giving us a dumbbell. In order to further simplify things, we assume that the rod is connected rigidly to a fixed axle at the center of mass of the two particles, as shown in figure 11.6. The masses constituting the ends of the dumbbell are therefore free to revolve in circles about the axle, but they are prevented from executing any other motion. The key effect of this constraint is that both masses rotate about the axle with the same angular frequency ω.

If the particles are respectively distances d_1 and d_2 from the axle, then their speeds are $v_1 = d_1\omega$ and $v_2 = d_2\omega$. Thus the kinetic energy of the rotating dumbbell is

$$K_{intern} = \frac{1}{2}M_1 v_1^2 + \frac{1}{2}M_2 v_2^2 = \frac{1}{2}I\omega^2 \quad \text{(fixed axle)}, \tag{11.16}$$

where $I = M_1 d_1^2 + M_2 d_2^2$ is called the *moment of inertia*. Similarly, the magnitude of the spin angular momentum, which is a vector parallel to the axle, is

$$L_{spin} = M_1 d_1 v_1 + M_2 d_2 v_2 = I\omega \quad \text{(fixed axle)}. \tag{11.17}$$

Finally, Newton's second law for rotation becomes

$$\tau = \frac{dL_{spin}}{dt} = \frac{dI\omega}{dt} = I\frac{d\omega}{dt} \quad \text{(fixed axle)}, \tag{11.18}$$

where τ is the component of torque along the rotation axis.

Note that the rightmost expression in equation (11.18) assumes that I is constant, which only is true if d_1 and d_2 are constant – i. e., the dumbbell must truly be rigid.

11.5 Many Particles

The generalization from two particles to many particles is quite easy in principle. If a subscripted i indicates the value of a quantity for the ith particle, then the center of mass is given by

$$\mathbf{R}_{cm} = \frac{1}{M_{total}} \sum_i M_i \mathbf{r}_i \tag{11.19}$$

where

$$M_{total} = \sum_i M_i. \tag{11.20}$$

Furthermore, if we define $\mathbf{r}_i' = \mathbf{r}_i - \mathbf{R}_{cm}$, etc., then the kinetic energy is just

$$K_{total} = M_{total} V_{cm}^2/2 + \sum_i M_i v_i'^2/2 \tag{11.21}$$

and the angular momentum is

$$\mathbf{L}_{total} = M_{total}\mathbf{R}_{cm} \times \mathbf{V}_{cm} + \sum_i M_i \mathbf{r}_i' \times \mathbf{v}_i'. \tag{11.22}$$

In other words, both the kinetic energy and the angular momentum can be separated into two parts: one part is related to the overall motion of the system and the other is due to motions of system components relative to the center of mass, just as for the case of the dumbbell.

11.6 Rigid Bodies

For a rigid body rotating about a fixed axle, the moment of inertia is

$$I = \sum_i M_i d_i^2, \tag{11.23}$$

where d_i is the perpendicular distance of the ith particle from the axle. Equations (11.16)-(11.18) are valid for a rigid body consisting of many particles. Furthermore, the moment of inertia is constant in this case, so it can be taken out of the time derivative:

$$\tau = \frac{dI\omega}{dt} = I\frac{d\omega}{dt} = I\alpha \quad \text{(fixed axle, constant } I\text{)}. \tag{11.24}$$

The quantity $\alpha = d\omega/dt$ is called the *angular acceleration*.

The sum in the equation for the moment of inertia can be converted to an integral for a continuous distribution of mass. We shall not pursue this here, but simply quote the results for a number of solid objects of uniform density:

- For rotation of a sphere of mass M and radius R about an axis piercing its center: $I = 2MR^2/5$.

- For rotation of a cylinder of mass M and radius R about its axis of symmetry: $I = MR^2/2$.

- For rotation of a thin rod of mass M and length L about an axis perpendicular to the rod passing through its center: $I = ML^2/12$.

- For rotation of an annulus of mass M, inner radius R_a, and outer radius R_b about its axis of symmetry: $I = M(R_a^2 + R_b^2)/2$.

11.7 Statics

If a rigid body is initially at rest, it will remain at rest if and only if the sum of all the forces and the sum of all the torques acting on the body are zero. As an example, a mass balance with arms of differing length is shown in figure 11.7. The balance beam is subject to three forces pointing upward or downward, the tension T in the string from which the beam is suspended and the weights M_1g and M_2g exerted on the beam by the two suspended

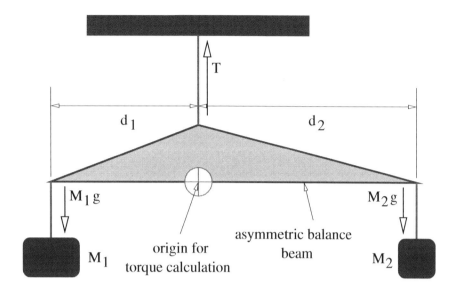

Figure 11.7: Asymmetric mass balance. We assume that the balance beam is massless.

masses. The parameter g is the local gravitational field and the balance beam itself is assumed to have negligible mass. Taking upward as positive, the force condition for static equilibrium is

$$T - M_1g - M_2g = 0 \quad \text{(zero net force)}. \tag{11.25}$$

Defining a counterclockwise torque to be positive, the torque balance computed about the pivot point in figure 11.7 is

$$\tau = M_1gd_1 - M_2gd_2 = 0 \quad \text{(zero torque)}, \tag{11.26}$$

where d_1 and d_2 are the lengths of the beam arms.

The first of the above equations shows that the tension in the string must be

$$T = (M_1 + M_2)g, \tag{11.27}$$

while the second shows that

$$\frac{M_1}{M_2} = \frac{d_2}{d_1}. \tag{11.28}$$

CHAPTER 11. ROTATIONAL DYNAMICS

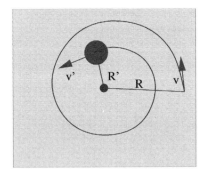

Figure 11.8: Trajectory of a mass on a frictionless table attached to a string which passes through a hole in the table. The string is drawing the mass in.

Thus, the tension in the string is just equal to the weight of the masses attached to the balance beam, while the ratio of the two masses equals the inverse ratio of the associated beam arm lengths.

11.8 Problems

1. Show using the component form of the cross product given by equation (11.4) that $\mathbf{A} \times \mathbf{B} = -\mathbf{B} \times \mathbf{A}$.

2. A mass M is sliding on a frictionless table, but is attached to a string which passes through a hole in the center of the table as shown in figure 11.8. The string is gradually drawn in so the mass traces out a spiral pattern as shown in figure 11.8. The initial distance of the mass from the hole in the table is R and its initial tangential velocity is v. After the string is drawn in, the mass is a distance R' from the hole and its tangential velocity is v'.

   (a) Given R, v, and R', find v'.

   (b) Compute the change in the kinetic energy of the mass in going from radius R to radius R'.

   (c) If the above change is non-zero, determine where the extra energy came from.

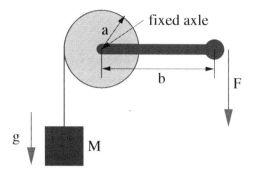

Figure 11.9: A crank on a fixed axle turns a drum, thus winding the rope around the drum and raising the mass.

3. A car of mass 1000 kg is heading north on a road at 30 m s^{-1} which passes 2 km east of the center of town.

   (a) Compute the angular momentum of the car about the center of town when the car is directly east of the town.

   (b) Compute the angular momentum of the car about the center of town when it is 3 km north of the above point.

4. The apparatus illustrated in figure 11.9 is used to raise a bucket of mass M out of a well.

   (a) What force F must be exerted to keep the bucket from falling back into the well?

   (b) If the bucket is slowly raised a distance d, what work is done on the bucket by the rope attached to it?

   (c) What work is done by the force F on the handle in the above case?

5. Derive equations (11.13) and (11.14).

6. A mass M is held up by the structure shown in figure 11.10. The support beam has negligible mass. Find the tension T in the diagonal wire. Hint: Compute the net torque on the support beam about point A due to the tension T and the weight of the mass M.

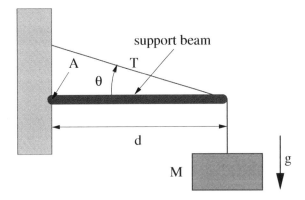

Figure 11.10: A mass is supported by the tension in the diagonal wire. The support beam is free to pivot at point A.

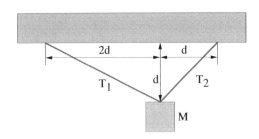

Figure 11.11: A mass is supported by two strings.

7. A system consists of two stars, one of mass M moving with velocity $\mathbf{v}_1 = (0, v, 0)$ at position $\mathbf{r}_1 = (d, 0, 0)$, the other of mass $2M$ with zero velocity at the origin.

   (a) Find the center of mass position and velocity of the system of two stars.

   (b) Find the spin angular momentum of the system.

   (c) Find the internal kinetic energy of the system.

8. A solid disk is rolling down a ramp tilted an angle θ from the horizontal. Compute the acceleration of the disk down the ramp and compare it

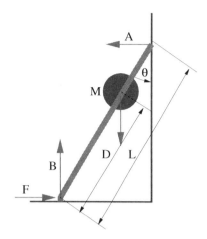

Figure 11.12: A ladder leaning against a wall is held in place the force F acting on the base of the ladder.

with the acceleration of a block sliding down the ramp without friction.

9. A mass M is suspended from the ceiling by two strings as shown in figure 11.11. Find the tensions in the strings.

10. A man of mass M is a distance D up a ladder of length L which makes an angle θ with respect to the vertical wall as shown in figure 11.12. Take the mass of the ladder to be negligible. Find the force F needed to keep the ladder from sliding if the wall and floor are frictionless and therefore can only exert normal forces A and B on the ladder.

Chapter 12

Harmonic Oscillator

Figure 12.1 illustrates the prototypical harmonic oscillator, the mass-spring system. A mass M is attached to one end of a spring. The other end of the spring is attached to something rigid such as a wall. The spring exerts a restoring force $F = -kx$ on the mass when it is stretched by an amount x, i. e., it acts to return the mass to its initial position. This is called *Hooke's law* and k is called the *spring constant*.

12.1 Energy Analysis

The potential energy of the mass-spring system is

$$U(x) = kx^2/2 \tag{12.1}$$

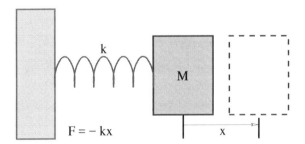

Figure 12.1: Illustration of a mass-spring system.

204

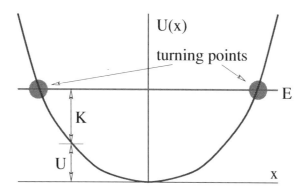

Figure 12.2: Potential, kinetic, and total energy of a harmonic oscillator plotted as a function of spring displacement x.

which may be verified by noting that the Hooke's law force is derived from this potential energy: $F = -d(kx^2/2)/dx = -kx$. This is shown in figure 12.2. Since a potential energy exists, the total energy $E = K+U$ is conserved, i. e., is constant in time. If the total energy is known, this provides a useful tool for determining how the kinetic energy varies with the position x of the mass M: $K(x) = E - U(x)$. Since the kinetic energy is expressed (nonrelativistically) in terms of the velocity u as $K = Mu^2/2$, the velocity at any point on the graph in figure 12.2 is

$$u = \pm \left(\frac{2(E - U)}{M} \right)^{1/2}. \tag{12.2}$$

Given all this, it is fairly evident how the mass moves. From Hooke's law, the mass is always *accelerating* toward the *equilibrium position, $x = 0$.* However, at any point the *velocity* can be either to the left or the right. At the points where $U(x) = E$, the kinetic energy is zero. This occurs at the turning points

$$x_{TP} = \pm \left(\frac{2E}{k} \right)^{1/2}. \tag{12.3}$$

If the mass is moving to the left, it slows down as it approaches the left turning point. It stops when it reaches this point and begins to move to the right. It accelerates until it passes the equilibrium position and then begins to decelerate, stopping at the right turning point, accelerating toward the left, etc. The mass thus oscillates between the left and right turning points. (Note that equations (12.2) and (12.3) are only true for the harmonic oscillator.)

How does the period of the oscillation depend on the total energy of the system? Notice that from equation (12.2) the maximum speed of the mass (i. e., the speed at $x = 0$) is equal to $u_{max} = (2E/M)^{1/2}$. The average speed must be some fraction of this maximum value. Let us guess here that it is half the maximum speed:

$$u_{average} \approx \frac{u_{max}}{2} = \left(\frac{E}{2M}\right)^{1/2} \quad \text{(approximate).} \tag{12.4}$$

However, the distance d the mass has to travel for one full oscillation is twice the distance between turning points, or $d = 4(2E/k)^{1/2}$. Therefore, the period of oscillation must be approximately

$$T = \frac{d}{u_{average}} \approx 4\left(\frac{2E}{k}\right)^{1/2}\left(\frac{2M}{E}\right)^{1/2} = 8\left(\frac{M}{k}\right)^{1/2} \quad \text{(approximate).} \tag{12.5}$$

12.2 Analysis Using Newton's Laws

The acceleration of the mass at any time is given by Newton's second law:

$$a = \frac{d^2x}{dt^2} = \frac{F}{M} = -\frac{kx}{M}. \tag{12.6}$$

An equation of this type is known as a *differential equation* since it involves a derivative of the dependent variable x. Equations of this type are generally more difficult to solve than algebraic equations, as there are no universal techniques for solving all forms of such equations. In fact, it is fair to say that the solutions of most differential equations were originally obtained by *guessing*!

We already have the basis on which to make an intelligent guess for the solution to equation (12.6) since we know that the mass oscillates back and forth with a period that is independent of the amplitude of the oscillation. A function which might fill the bill is the cosine function. Let us try substituting $x = \cos(\omega t)$, where ω is a constant, into this equation. The second derivative of x with respect to t is $-\omega^2 \cos(\omega t)$, so performing this substitution results in

$$-\omega^2 \cos(\omega t) = -\frac{k}{M}\cos(\omega t). \tag{12.7}$$

Notice that the cosine function cancels out, leaving us with $-\omega^2 = -k/M$. The guess thus works if we set

$$\omega = \left(\frac{k}{M}\right)^{1/2}. \tag{12.8}$$

The constant ω is the angular oscillation frequency for the oscillator, from which we infer the period of oscillation to be $T = 2\pi(M/k)^{1/2}$. This agrees with the earlier approximate result of equation (12.5), except that the approximation has a numerical factor of 8 rather than $2\pi \approx 6$. Thus, the earlier guess is only off by about 30%!

It is easy to show that $x = B\cos(\omega t)$ is also a solution of equation (12.6), where B is any constant and $\omega = (k/M)^{1/2}$. This confirms that the oscillation frequency and period are independent of amplitude. Furthermore, the sine function is equally valid as a solution: $x = A\sin(\omega t)$, where A is another constant. In fact, the most general possible solution is just a combination of these two, i. e.,

$$x = A\sin(\omega t) + B\cos(\omega t) = C\cos(\omega t - \phi). \tag{12.9}$$

The values of A and B depend on the position and velocity of the mass at time $t = 0$. The right side of equation (12.9) shows an alternate way of writing the general harmonic oscillator solution that uses a cosine function with a phase factor ϕ.

12.3 Forced Oscillator

If we wiggle the left end of the spring by the amount $d = d_0\cos(\omega_F t)$, as in figure 12.3, rather than rigidly fixing it as in figure 12.1, we have a *forced* harmonic oscillator. The constant d_0 is the amplitude of the imposed wiggling motion. The *forcing frequency* ω_F is not necessarily equal to the natural or *resonant* frequency $\omega = (k/M)^{1/2}$ of the mass-spring system. Very different behavior occurs depending on whether ω_F is less than, equal to, or greater than ω.

Given the above wiggling, the force of the spring on the mass becomes $F = -k(x - d) = -k[x - d_0\cos(\omega_F t)]$ since the length of the spring is the difference between the positions of the left and right ends. Proceeding as for

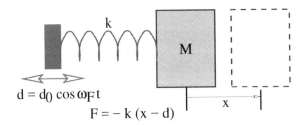

Figure 12.3: Illustration of a forced mass-spring oscillator. The left end of the spring is wiggled back and forth with an angular frequency ω_F and a maximum amplitude d_0.

the unforced mass-spring system, we arrive at the differential equation

$$\frac{d^2 x}{dt^2} + \frac{kx}{M} = \frac{kd_0}{M} \cos(\omega_F t). \qquad (12.10)$$

The solution to this equation turns out to be the sum of a forced part in which x is proportional to $\cos(\omega_F t)$ and a free part which is the same as the solution to the unforced equation (12.9). We are primarily interested in the forced part of the solution, so let us set $x = x_0 \cos(\omega_F t)$ and substitute this into equation (12.10):

$$-\omega_F^2 x_0 \cos(\omega_F t) + \frac{kx_0}{M} \cos(\omega_F t) = \frac{kd_0}{M} \cos(\omega_F t). \qquad (12.11)$$

Again the cosine factor cancels and we are left with an algebraic equation for x_0, the amplitude of the oscillatory motion of the mass.

Solving for the ratio of the oscillation amplitude of the mass to the amplitude of the wiggling motion, x_0/d_0, we find

$$\frac{x_0}{d_0} = \frac{1}{1 - \omega_F^2/\omega^2}, \qquad (12.12)$$

where we have recognized that $k/M = \omega^2$, the square of the frequency of the *free* oscillation. This function is plotted in figure 12.4.

Notice that if $\omega_F < \omega$, the motion of the mass is in phase with the wiggling motion and the amplitude of the mass oscillation is greater than the amplitude of the wiggling. As the forcing frequency approaches the natural frequency of the oscillator, the response of the mass grows in amplitude.

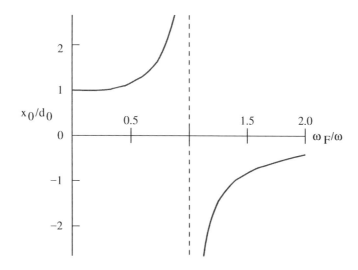

Figure 12.4: Plot of the ratio of response to forcing vs. the ratio of forced to free oscillator frequency for the mass-spring system.

When the forcing is at the resonant frequency, the response is technically infinite, though practical limits on the amplitude of the oscillation will intervene in this case — for instance, the spring cannot stretch or shrink an infinite amount. In many cases friction will act to limit the response of the mass to forcing near the resonant frequency. When the forcing frequency is greater than the natural frequency, the mass actually moves in the opposite direction of the wiggling motion — i. e., the response is out of phase with the forcing. The amplitude of the response decreases as the forcing frequency increases above the resonant frequency.

Forced and free harmonic oscillators form an important part of many physical systems. For instance, any elastic material body such as a bridge or an airplane wing has harmonic oscillatory modes. A common engineering problem is to ensure that such modes are damped by friction or some other physical mechanism when there is a possibility of exitation of these modes by naturally occurring processes. A number of disasters can be traced to a failure to properly account for oscillatory forcing in engineered structures.

12.4 Complex Exponential Solutions

Complex exponential functions of the form $x = \exp(\pm i\omega t)$ also constitute solutions to the free harmonic oscillator governed by equation (12.6). This makes sense, as the complex exponential is the sum of sines and cosines. However, for the frictionless harmonic oscillator, the exponential solutions provide no particular advantage over sines and cosines. Furthermore, oscillator displacements are real, not complex quantities.

The superposition principle solves the problem of complex versus real solutions. For an equation like (12.6) which has real coefficients, if $\exp(i\omega t)$ is a solution, then so is $\exp(-i\omega t)$, so the superposition of these two solutions is also a solution. Furthermore

$$\exp(i\omega t) + \exp(-i\omega t) = 2\cos(\omega t) = 2\text{Re}[\exp(i\omega t)]. \tag{12.13}$$

This shows a shortcut for getting the physical part of a complex exponential solution to equations like the harmonic oscillator equation; simply take the real part.

Complex exponential solutions come into their own for more complicated equations. For instance, suppose the force on the mass in the mass-spring system takes the form

$$F = -kx - b\frac{dx}{dt}. \tag{12.14}$$

The term containing b represents a frictional damping effect on the harmonic oscillator and the governing differential equation becomes

$$\frac{d^2x}{dt^2} + \frac{b}{M}\frac{dx}{dt} + \frac{k}{M}x = 0. \tag{12.15}$$

Trying the exponential function $\exp(\sigma t)$ in this equation results in

$$\sigma = \frac{1}{2}\left[-\frac{b}{M} \pm \left(\frac{b^2}{M^2} - \frac{4k}{M}\right)^{1/2}\right] = -\beta \pm i(\omega_0^2 - \beta^2)^{1/2} \tag{12.16}$$

where we have set

$$\beta = \frac{b}{2M} \qquad \omega_0 = \left(\frac{k}{M}\right)^{1/2}. \tag{12.17}$$

The quantity $\omega \equiv (\omega_0^2 - \beta^2)^{1/2}$ is the actual frequency of oscillation of the damped oscillator, which one can see is less than the oscillation frequency

ω_0 that occurs with the damping turned off. The physical solution to the damped oscillator is thus

$$x(t) = \text{Re}[\exp(\sigma t)] = \text{Re}[\exp(i\omega t)\exp(-\beta t)] = \cos(\omega t)\exp(-\beta t) \quad (12.18)$$

as long as $\omega_0^2 > \beta^2$. Notice that this solution is in the form of an oscillation $\cos(\omega t)$ multiplied by a decaying exponential $\exp(-\beta t)$. This confirms that the b term decreases the amplitude of the oscillation with time.

12.5 Quantum Mechanical Harmonic Oscillator

The quantum mechanical harmonic oscillator shares the characteristic of other quantum mechanical bound state problems in that the total energy can take on only discrete values. Calculation of these values is too difficult for this book, but the problem is sufficiently important to warrant reporting the results here. The energies accessible to a quantum mechanical mass-spring system are given by the formula

$$E_n = (n + 1/2)\hbar(k/M)^{1/2}, \quad n = 0, 1, 2, \ldots. \quad (12.19)$$

In other words, the energy *difference* between successive quantum mechanical energy levels in this case is constant and equals the classical resonant frequency for the oscillator, $\omega = (k/M)^{1/2}$, times $\hbar$.

12.6 Problems

1. An oscillator (non-harmonic) has the potential energy function $U(x) = Cx^4$, where C is a constant. How does the oscillation frequency depend on energy? Explain your reasoning.

2. Show that $C\cos(\omega t - \phi)$ is an alternate way of writing $A\sin(\omega t) + B\cos(\omega t)$ by finding the values of A and B in terms of the constants C and ϕ. Hint: Expand $\cos(\omega t - \phi)$ by using the trigonometric identity for the cosine of the sum of two angles.

3. If a mass-spring harmonic oscillator has displacement $x = 0$ and velocity $dx/dt = V$ at time $t = 0$, determine the values of A and B as well as those of C and ϕ in equation (12.9).

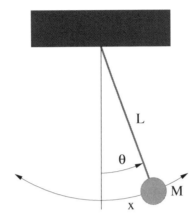

Figure 12.5: The pendulum as a harmonic oscillator.

4. A mass M is suspended against gravity by a spring of spring constant k. The unstretched length of the spring is x_0 and under the influence of gravity the spring is stretched to a resting length $x_1 > x_0$.

   (a) Compute the length of the spring x_1 in the steady, resting case.

   (b) Set up the equation of motion for the mass moving under the influence of the two forces, gravity and spring. Solve the equation for the frequency of the oscillation and the position of the spring as a function of time $x(t)$. Does the oscillation frequency change from the case without gravity?

5. Determine the two real solutions to the damped harmonic oscillator problem in the case in which $\omega_0^2 < \beta^2$.

6. Consider the pendulum in figure 12.5. The mass M moves along an arc with x denoting the distance along the arc from the equilibrium point.

   (a) Find the component of the gravitational force tangent to the arc (and thus in the direction of motion of the mass) as a function of the angle θ. Use the small angle approximation on $\sin(\theta)$ to simplify this answer.

   (b) Get the force in terms of x rather than θ. (Recall that $\theta = x/L$.)

(c) Use Newton's second law for motion in the x direction (i. e., along the arc followed by the mass) to get the equation of motion for the mass.

(d) Solve the equation of motion using the solution to the mass-spring problem as a guide.

7. Forced damped oscillator:

(a) Add a damping term to the forced harmonic oscillator equation (12.10) and solve for the forced part of the solution using complex exponential methods. Hint: Change the cosine on the right side of this equation to $\exp(i\omega_F t)$ to convert the equation to complex form and then try the solution $x = x_0 \exp(i\omega_F t)$ where x_0 will depend on ω_F. Also, write the equation in terms of $\beta = b/(2M)$ and $\omega^2 = k/M$.

(b) Find the physical part of this solution by taking the real part of $x(t)$. Hint: While taking the real part of x, it may be helpful to recall that the inverse of any complex number can be written $1/(a+ib) = (a-ib)/(a^2+b^2)$.

(c) Determine how x_0 differs from that in the undamped case when ω_F is near the resonant frequency of the unforced oscillator. In particular, show how the phase and amplitude of the oscillation change as the forcing frequency changes from less than to greater than the resonant frequency.

8. A *massless* particle is confined to a box of length a. (Think of a photon between two mirrors.) Treating the particle classically, compute the period of one round trip from one end of the box to the other and back again. From this compute an angular frequency for the oscillation of this particle in the box. Does this frequency depend on the particle's energy?

9. Compute the ground state energy E_{ground} of a massless particle in a box of length a using quantum mechanics. Compare $E_{ground}/\hbar$ with the angular frequency computed in the previous problem.

Appendix A

Constants, Units, and Conversions

This appendix contains various useful constants and conversion factors as well as information on the International System of Units.

A.1 SI Units

"SI" is the French abbreviation for the International System of Units, the system used universally in science. See http://physics.nist.gov/cuu/Units/ for the last word on this subject. This treatment is derived from the National Institute of Science and Technology (NIST) website.

The most fundamental units of measure are length (meters; m), mass (kilograms; kg), time (seconds; s), electric current (ampere; A), temperature (kelvin; K), amount of a substance (mole; mol), and the luminous intensity (candela; cd). The candela is a rather specialized unit related to the perceived brightness of a light source by a "standard" human eye. As such, it is rather anthropocentric and hardly seems to merit the designation "fundamental". The mole is also less fundamental than the other units, as it is simply a convenient way to refer to a multiple of Avogadro's number of atoms or molecules.

Fundamental units can be combined to form derived units with special names. Some of these derived units are listed below.

Fundamental and derived SI units can have multipliers expressed as prefixes, e. g., 1 km = 1000 m. The NIST website points out a minor irregularity with the fundamental unit of mass, the kilogram. This already has the multiplier "kilo" prefixed to the unit "gram". In this case 1000 kg is written 1 Mg, not 1 kkg, etc. SI multipliers are listed below as well.

A.1.1 Derived Units

Name	Abbrev.	Units	Meaning
hertz	Hz	s^{-1}	frequency (cycles/sec)
(unnamed)		s^{-1}	angular frequency (radians/sec)
newton	N	$kg\ m\ s^{-2}$	force
pascal	Pa	$N\ m^{-2}$	pressure
joule	J	$N\ m$	energy
watt	W	$J\ s^{-1}$	power
coulomb	C	$A\ s$	electric charge
volt	V	$N\ m\ C^{-1}$	scalar potential
(unnamed)		$N\ s\ C^{-1}$	vector potential
(unnamed)		$V\ m^{-1}$	electric field
tesla	T	$N\ s\ C^{-1}\ m^{-1}$	magnetic field
(unnamed)		$V\ m$	electric flux
weber	Wb	$T\ m^2$	magnetic flux
volt	V	V	electric circulation (EMF)
(unnamed)		$T\ m$	magnetic circulation
farad	F	$C\ V^{-1}$	capacitance
ohm	Ω	$V\ A^{-1}$	resistance
henry	H	$V\ s^2\ C^{-1}$	inductance

A.1.2   SI Multipliers

Multiplier	Name	Prefix
10^{24}	yotta	Y
10^{21}	zetta	Z
10^{18}	exa	E
10^{15}	peta	P
10^{12}	tera	T
10^{9}	giga	G
10^{6}	mega	M
10^{3}	kilo	k
10^{2}	hecto	h
10^{1}	deka	da
10^{-1}	deci	d
10^{-2}	centi	c
10^{-3}	milli	m
10^{-6}	micro	μ
10^{-9}	nano	n
10^{-12}	pico	p
10^{-15}	femto	f
10^{-18}	atto	a
10^{-21}	zepto	z
10^{-24}	yocto	y

A.1.3   CGS or Centimeter-Gram-Second Units

An older system of scientific units is the CGS system. This system is still used widely in certain areas of physics. The fundamental units of length, mass, and time are as implied by the title given above. The most common CGS derived units are those for force (1 dyne $= 10^{-5}$ N) and energy (1 erg $= 10^{-7}$ J).

Electromagnetism is expressed in several different ways in CGS units. Electromagnetic quantities in CGS not only have different units than in SI, they also have different physical dimensions, with different versions differing among themselves. The most common variant of CGS electromagnetic units is called "Gaussian" units. This variant is advocated by some physicists, though many others consider the whole subject of CGS electromagnetic units to be a terrible mess! SI units for electromagnetism are used in this text and

CGS units will not be discussed further here.

A.1.4 Miscellaneous Conversions

1 lb = 4.448 N
1 ft = 0.3048 m
1 mph = 0.4470 m s^{-1}
1 eV = 1.60×10^{-19} J
1 mol = 6.022×10^{23} molecules
(One mole of carbon-12 atoms has a mass of 12 g.)
1 gauss = 10^{-4} T (CGS unit of magnetic field)
1 millibar = 1 mb = 100 Pa (Old unit of pressure)

A.2 Advice on Calculations

A.2.1 Substituting Numbers

When faced with solving an algebraic equation to obtain a numerical answer, solve the equation symbolically first and then substitute numbers. For example, given the equation

$$ax^2 - b = 0 \tag{A.1}$$

where $a = 2$ and $b = 8$, first solve for x,

$$x = \pm(b/a)^{1/2}, \tag{A.2}$$

and then substitute the numerical values:

$$x = \pm(8/2)^{1/2} = \pm4^{1/2} = \pm2. \tag{A.3}$$

This procedure is far better than substituting numbers first,

$$2x^2 - 8 = 0, \tag{A.4}$$

and then solving for x. Solving first and then substituting has two advantages: (1) It is easier to make algebraic manipulations with symbols than it is with numbers. (2) If you decide later that numerical values should be different, then the entire solution procedure doesn't have to be repeated, only the substitutions at the end.

A.2.2 Significant Digits

In numerical calculations, keep only one additional digit beyond those present in the least accurate input number. For instance, if you are taking the square root of 3.4, your calculator might tell you that the answer is 1.843908891. The answer you write down should be 1.84. Keeping all ten digits of the calculator's answer gives a false sense of the accuracy of the result.

Round the result up if the digit following the last significant digit is 5 or greater and round it down if it is less than 5. Thus, the square root of 4.1, which the calculator tells us is 2.049390153, should be represented as 2.05 rather than 2.04.

A.2.3 Changing Units

It is easy to make mistakes when changing the units of a quantity. Adopting a systematic approach to changing units greatly reduces the chance of error. We illustrate a systematic approach to this problem with an example in which we change the units of acceleration from meters per second squared to kilometers per minute squared:

$$
\begin{aligned}
5 \text{ m/s}^2 \quad \rightarrow \quad & 5 \text{ m/s}^2 \times (0.001 \text{ km/m}) \times (60 \text{ s/min})^2 \\
= \quad & 5 \times 0.001 \times 60^2 \text{ km/min}^2 \\
= \quad & 18 \text{ km/min}^2.
\end{aligned}
\tag{A.5}
$$

The trick is to multiply by the conversion factor for each unit to the power that makes the original unit cancel out. The conversion factors to the proper powers are then multiplied by the original number and the proper cancellations of the old units are double checked. If done with care, this yields the correct result every time!

A.3   Constants of Nature

Symbol	Value	Meaning
h	6.63×10^{-34} J s	Planck's constant
$\hbar$	1.06×10^{-34} J s	$h/(2\pi)$
c	2.998×10^{8} m s^{-1}	speed of light
G	6.67×10^{-11} m^3 s^{-2} kg^{-1}	universal gravitational constant
k_B	1.38×10^{-23} J K^{-1}	Boltzmann's constant
σ	5.67×10^{-8} W m^{-2} K^{-4}	Stefan-Boltzmann constant
K	3.67×10^{11} s^{-1} K^{-1}	thermal frequency constant
ϵ_0	8.85×10^{-12} C^2 N^{-1} m^{-2}	permittivity of free space
μ_0	$4\pi \times 10^{-7}$ N s^2 C^{-2}	permeability of free space $(= 1/(\epsilon_0 c^2))$.

A.4   Properties of Stable Particles

Symbol	Value	Meaning
e	1.60×10^{-19} C	fundamental unit of charge
m_e	9.11×10^{-31} kg $= 0.511$ MeV	mass of electron
m_p	1.672648×10^{-27} kg $= 938.280$ MeV	mass of proton
m_n	1.674954×10^{-27} kg $= 939.573$ MeV	mass of neutron

A.5   Properties of Solar System Objects

Symbol	Value	Meaning
M_e	5.98×10^{24} kg	mass of earth
M_m	7.36×10^{22} kg	mass of moon
M_s	1.99×10^{30} kg	mass of sun
R_e	6.37×10^{6} m	radius of earth
R_m	1.74×10^{6} m	radius of moon
R_s	6.96×10^{8} m	radius of sun
D_m	3.82×10^{8} m	earth-moon distance
D_s	1.50×10^{11} m	earth-sun distance
g	9.81 m s^{-2}	earth's surface gravity

Index

Made in the USA
San Bernardino, CA
25 July 2016